HEALTH
AND DISEASE

LIFE SCIENCE LIBRARY

CONSULTING EDITORS
René Dubos
Henry Margenau
C. P. Snow

HEALTH AND DISEASE

by René Dubos, Maya Pines

and the Editors of LIFE

TIME INCORPORATED, NEW YORK

ABOUT THIS BOOK

IN THE POPULAR MIND, disease is usually attributed to germs. The fact is, as this book makes clear, that disease results from a complicated interaction between man and his environment. The food he eats, the air he breathes, the genetic traits he was born with, the physical and mental stresses he endures, no less than the microbes to which he is exposed, all help determine whether he will be healthy or sickly.

In this book each chapter of the text is followed by a picture essay; the essay supplements the text, but each may be read independently. For example, Chapter 5, "The Insidious Poisons," deals with the problem of environmental pollution; the following essay, "The Pollutions of a City," details the causes of the problem and the attempts that have been made to deal with it in America's largest metropolis.

THE AUTHORS

RENE DUBOS, scientist and author, is particularly concerned with the relationship between disease and environment— a field in which he is one of the few authorities. He is also a consulting editor of the LIFE Science Library (below).

MAYA PINES is a writer specializing in the social aspects of medicine and education. Her articles have appeared in *Harper's*, *The Reporter* and *The New York Times Magazine*. She is also the coauthor of a book, *Retarded Children Can Be Helped*.

THE CONSULTING EDITORS

RENE DUBOS, member and professor of The Rockefeller University, is a microbiologist and experimental pathologist famous for his work in antibiotics, including the discovery of tyrothricin. He has written, among other books, *Mirage of Health*, *The Dreams of Reason* and *Man Adapting*.

HENRY MARGENAU is Eugene Higgins Professor of Physics and Natural Philosophy at Yale, an editor of the *American Journal of Science*, and a notable contributor to spectroscopy and nuclear physics. He has written *Open Vistas, The Nature of Physical Reality,* and is coauthor of *The Scientist* in this series.

C. P. SNOW, physicist and author, has won acclaim for his many novels, among them *The Affair* and *Corridors of Power*, which explore the relationship between the scientist and the rest of modern society. As Lord Snow, he was named to the British Ministry of Technology in 1964.

ON THE COVER

Rice stalks, flies and a syringe suggest the wide variety of things in man's environment that affect his health. Rice represents a source of nutrition, a vital factor in health; flies are among the many creatures that carry infectious microbes; the syringe and other medical weapons help in the prevention and treatment of disease. The drawing on the back cover indicates the strong influence of external forces on the body's interior condition.

CONTENTS

TIME-LIFE BOOKS

EDITOR
Norman P. Ross

EXECUTIVE EDITOR
Maitland A. Edey

TEXT DIRECTOR   ART DIRECTOR
Jerry Korn   Edward A. Hamilton

CHIEF OF RESEARCH
Beatrice T. Dobie

Assistant Text Director: Harold C. Field
Assistant Art Director: Arnold C. Holeywell
Assistant Chiefs of Research:
Monica O. Horne, Martha Turner

PUBLISHER
Rhett Austell

General Manager: Joseph C. Hazen Jr.
Planning Director: Frank M. White
Business Manager: John D. McSweeney
Circulation Manager: Joan D. Manley
Publishing Board: Nicholas Benton,
Louis Bronzo, James Wendell Forbes,
John S. Wiseman

LIFE MAGAZINE

EDITOR: Edward K. Thompson
MANAGING EDITOR: George P. Hunt
PUBLISHER: Jerome S. Hardy

LIFE SCIENCE LIBRARY

SERIES EDITOR: Martin Mann
Editorial staff for *Health and Disease:*
Associate Editor: Robert G. Mason
Text Editors: Neal G. Stuart, Alfred Lansing,
Nancy E. Gross, Ogden Tanner
Picture Editor: Simone Daro Gossner
Designer: Arnold C. Holeywell
Associate Designer: Edwin Taylor
Staff Writers: Tom Alexander, Samuel Halper,
Jonathan Kastner, Harvey B. Loomis,
Charles Osborne
Chief Researcher: Thelma C. Stevens
Researchers: Leah Dunaief, Rosemary Dies,
Elizabeth Evans, Owen Fang, Ann Ferebee,
Helen Greenway, Donald Hinkle, John Hochmann,
Alice Kantor, Irene J. Kleinsinger, Suzanne Massie,
Marianna Pinchot, Susanna Seymour
EDITORIAL PRODUCTION
Color Director: Robert L. Young
Copy Staff: Marian Gordon Goldman,
Suzanne Seixas, Dolores A. Littles
Picture Bureau: Margaret K. Goldsmith,
Joan Lynch
Art Assistants: James D. Smith, Patricia Byrne,
Charles Mikolaycak, Douglas B. Graham

The text for the chapters of this book was written by René Dubos and Maya Pines, and for the picture essays by the editorial staff. The following individuals and departments of Time Inc. were helpful in the production of the book: Larry Burrows, Fritz Goro, Carl Mydans and Arthur Rickerby, LIFE staff photographers; Doris O'Neil, Chief, LIFE Picture Library; Richard M. Clurman, Chief, TIME-LIFE News Service; and Peter Draz, Chief, Time Inc. Bureau of Editorial Reference.

INTRODUCTION

PRIMITIVE MAN took a quite fatalistic view of life, death and that gray area of disease that lies between. Sickness, although mysterious, was too familiar to be regarded as a mystery. It was a part of nature and, therefore, a part of life. It was something to be endured.

Had our forefathers been minded to define health and disease, they might have reflected that they considered themselves to be in good health as long as they were able to cope effectively with the world around them and were at ease in it. They suffered disease to the extent that the stresses of their worlds became too much for them. Expressed in the language of our day, a man is healthy when he is in harmony with his environment, he is sick when discord prevails.

It was not until the middle of the 19th Century that man's understanding of nature grew to the point of justifying the faith that he could, by taking thought and action, bring the major environmental hazards to health under his control. Another half century was to elapse before the achievements of sanitary engineering and preventive medicine in adapting the environment to man were complemented by the successes of therapeutic medicine in helping man to adapt himself.

But nature is a jealous partner. She exacts a price from those who presume to reorder her ways with the human organism that she designed or with the world in which she placed it. Our civilization has long since decided that technological progress is worth the price. We accept the stresses of industrialization and urbanization, the carnage of the highways, the threat of radioactive fallout and the hazards of exposure to the noxious chemicals that are so freely discharged into our environment. There is also a price to be paid for medical progress. The physician commands powerful tools that he knows how to use only imperfectly and his judgments will not always be right.

These by-products of man's pursuit of technical and medical advancement are social as well as professional problems. They involve difficult ethical and moral choices. As a member of society the intelligent citizen has an obligation to seek to understand them. As a humanist he also has the privilege of questioning whether in our effort to add to the comfort and the quantity of our years we may be sacrificing some of their quality—whether the ways in which we are artificially reordering ourselves and our environment may not in some degree diminish our stature in nature and, thereby, rob life of some of its richness.

This luminous and gracious book recounts the story of health and disease in ways that are mindful of the quality as well as the quantity of life. I commend it to all who seek a better understanding of their place and of the place of their fellows in a world that they have increasing power to shape.

—R. KEITH CANNAN
Chairman, Division of Medical Sciences
National Academy of Sciences—National Research Council

1

The Body's Hazardous "Wisdom"

A TRIBUTE TO PROGRESS IN HEALTH
A Swedish man and wife sit for their 50th-wedding-anniversary portrait beneath a picture taken on their wedding day. At 71 and 74 respectively, they have achieved almost exactly the present life expectancy of the Swedish male and female at birth—the highest in the world. But the Swedish birthright of good health and a long life still eludes the majority of mankind.

IN MANY OLD NEW ENGLAND CHURCHYARDS, half the graves are those of children. Often these tiny headstones surround a larger one, marking the burial place of a mother who perished while still of childbearing age. And amid three or four such clusters there may be one large tombstone, bearing the name of the head of a family who, having survived a succession of wives and children, lived to a ripe old age.

Until the middle of the 19th Century, only half of all the children born in the U.S. reached their fifth year, and as recently as 1900 a newborn infant in the U.S. had less chance of surviving a week than did a man of 90. In earlier times, the figures were comparably shocking. England's Queen Anne, who reigned from 1702 to 1714, was a particularly unfortunate woman: she lost 16 of her 17 children as babies, and the sole survivor died before he was 12.

Compare that with the situation today. Since 1850, the most spectacular progress in health has been the drop in infant mortality. In the economically developed nations, 97 per cent of newborns live to adulthood. Few children suffer the effects of hunger. Few are infested with worms or other debilitating parasites. Today's youngsters are spared most of the infectious illnesses—smallpox, scarlet fever, dysentery—that carried off so many in the past. Of the 10 leading causes of death in infants and young children in 1850, every one has been brought under control. At the same time, childbirth is no longer the dangerous ordeal it once was. Today, very few mothers die in the process of delivery, although mortality rates were relatively high as recently as the 1930s.

Indeed, very few persons of any age or sex die of the acute infections which used to account for the majority of all deaths. Great epidemics are now rare. Life expectancy at birth has nearly doubled. From the mortality statistics, it would appear that modern medicine is well on the way to the conquest of disease.

It is true that advances in health in the last century have been little short of revolutionary. Nevertheless, disease is far from conquered, and there is little likelihood that it ever will be. All living things are diseased to some extent. Crops, lawns, household pets, the healthiest-looking human beings—all suffer from some disorders or from some infections. Even the bacteria that infect humans may themselves be infected with still-smaller organisms. Just as a garden always faces new onslaughts of weeds and pests, so the human race, after it has rooted out one disease, is assailed by another. Only the pattern of disease changes with changing times and changing cultures.

Even with increased bed space, U.S. hospitals are as crowded today as they ever were. Infectious illnesses send the same percentage of people to the hospital today as they did 50 years ago, although they kill far fewer people. Moreover, some 19 million Americans are at least partially incapacitated by one or more of the chronic diseases—arthritis, heart disease, diabetes. The percentage of these illnesses has risen alarmingly. As more people survive to old age, this trend will probably continue, filling homes, hospitals and nursing homes with helpless old people whom medicine can keep alive but not make well. In the Western world, the old pattern of death from infections has given way to a new pattern of death from the chronic diseases of later life.

The dream of a long life has always had a universal fascination. A century ago it was believed that medical science could raise the human lifespan to 150 or 200 years. Today's mortality statistics can be misinterpreted to suggest that longevity has already increased by more than 20 years since the mid-19th Century. And it is true that in the prosperous nations, many more people survive to adulthood than ever before. But once past 45, an American's life expectancy is not much greater now than it was in 1900. Today a man of 45 can expect to live to 72, a gain of only three years over 1900, while a woman of the same age can expect to live to 77, a gain of seven years.

Even good health is a relative term, hard to define in any general way. The people of Tristan da Cunha, a volcanic island in the Atlantic, are vigorous and active; they brave the roughest waters, climb up and down steep mountains and rarely seek medical assistance. Yet by Western standards most of them are unhealthy, often suffering from infestations of worms and from anemia. By the same token, an American city dweller who had a congenital dislocation of the hip, which usually leads to a painful arthritic condition by age 40, would consider himself sorely afflicted—but among the Navajos this dislocation is common, and it is not considered a disease.

Good health may mean different things to an astronaut and a fashion model, to a lumberjack and a Wall Street broker. Their ways of life require different levels of physical activity; their food needs and stresses vary, and they are not equally vulnerable to all diseases.

A new definition of health

Thus it is clear that the real measure of health is not the Utopian absence of all disease, but the ability to function effectively within a given environment. And since the environment keeps changing, good health is a process of continuous adaptation to the myriad microbes, irritants, pressures and problems which daily challenge man. This book will concern itself with an examination of this process of adaptation.

The body often comes to terms with its changing environment in ways that are scarcely apparent to the individual. Confrontation with sudden cold, for example, sets all kinds of internal mechanisms to work to neutralize its effects and keep the body on an even keel. In order to prevent

INFANT MORTALITY in the 18th Century U.S. was so high that 50 per cent of all deaths in the late 1700s were of children under 10. This touching tombstone carving in a Rockingham, Vermont, cemetery reflects the hard New England conditions of the time. The stone's inscription reads: "Sally Morrison, 1799, and two children, 1792 and 1798."

body temperature from dropping, the whole system undergoes certain changes designed to prevent loss of heat through the skin. Nearly all perspiration stops. The blood vessels near the surface of the body constrict, slowing the flow of blood from the inner regions, so that less reaches the skin and becomes cold. Another reflex, gooseflesh, has little practical value today, but must date back to the early days of the race, when the human animal had a covering of thick hair which, by standing on end, enclosed a protective layer of warmer air. If all the body's measures fail to prevent a drop in temperature, it initiates two more: the adrenal glands secrete more epinephrine, and the individual shivers, both of which serve to produce more heat.

"The laws of life"

The first man to draw scientific attention to these mechanisms was Claude Bernard, the father of modern physiology. Bernard distinguished himself by applying the experimental method to physiological research. At the same time that Charles Darwin was formulating the doctrine of evolution, Bernard advanced equally fruitful concepts in physiology, which he called "the science of the laws of life." His most popular work, *Introduction to the Study of Experimental Medicine*, was published in 1865. Darwinism holds that only those individuals and species survive and multiply which are fitted to their external environments. Bernard went one step further, describing this fitness as the ability to adapt to external changes while maintaining a constant internal environment. In this sense, fitness depends on the existence of control mechanisms which permit the organism to maintain its individuality in the face of all challenges. In Bernard's famous phrase, "The fixity of the internal environment is the essential requirement for a free life."

Later research in biochemistry confirmed this view. It provided laboratory evidence that the chemical composition of the healthy body's tissues and fluids does remain constant within extremely narrow limits, regardless of external conditions, and it unraveled the chemical processes through which this constancy is maintained. In the second decade of the 20th Century, Harvard's renowned Professor of Physiology, Walter B. Cannon, showed that these processes are largely controlled by the autonomic nervous system and by the hormones, body chemicals that mediate the behavior of the various organs and organ systems.

So impressed was Dr. Cannon with the extraordinary efficiency of these mechanisms that when he wrote a book in 1932 summarizing his thoughts, he called it *The Wisdom of the Body*. In this book he coined the word now generally used to describe the state produced by the constant adjustments the healthy body makes: "homeostasis," a term derived from the Greek words that mean "staying the same."

THE SELF-REGULATING NATURE of the body's chemical reactions was first recognized by the French physiologist Claude Bernard, shown here in a contemporary print testing a rabbit's physiological reactions to stimulation with an electric needle. Bernard's findings, based on many experiments with animals, laid the basis for modern physiology.

"The word does not imply something set and immobile," Dr. Cannon explained. "It means a condition—a condition which may vary, but which is relatively constant." And he went on to describe the intricate sequences by which the body maintains homeostasis in respect to such vital matters as oxygen, water, salts, temperature and blood pressure.

The body's wisdom has its limits. To begin with, the mechanisms for homeostasis do not emerge full-blown; it takes some time before they are developed in the newborn baby. In the womb, the amniotic fluid and the heat of the mother's body form an external environment virtually identical with that of the fetus' own interior. It is only at birth that the baby comes into contact with surroundings that demand constant adjustments. At first, even a small drop in the external temperature will produce a sharp drop in the infant's temperature. But little by little he develops the control mechanisms that enable him to handle outside temperature changes with ease.

"The golden age"

When he is about five, the child enters the most adaptable phase of life, "the golden age of resistance," which continues until he is 15 years old. In these years the mortality rate for nearly every infectious disease is at its lowest. The body's ability to mobilize its forces with precision remains high through the early twenties (nearly all speed records for the 100-yard dash have been set by men who were scarcely out of their teens) and to some extent in the thirties. But then this efficiency begins to wane. For example, as organisms grow older their heat-producing mechanisms tend to run down. By the time a man is 70, his rate of metabolism is generally 25 per cent lower than it was in early adulthood, and the homeostatic mechanisms function less efficiently. He can still maintain his body temperature at the proper level, but with greater difficulty. Moreover, because his body produces less heat and because his vascular system is less efficient, he is ill suited to sudden cold. Unless he compensates for these inadequacies by wearing warm clothing, he may be unable to maintain homeostasis, and he will become ill.

Conversely, and for similar reasons, old people find it difficult to get rid of body heat when the outside temperature becomes too warm. The homeostatic mechanisms which regulate the body's storage and use of sugar, and those which maintain the chemical balance of blood, become limited in their response to change as life goes on.

When all the homeostatic mechanisms are functioning efficiently, every challenge the body meets is handled in such a fashion as to prevent disease and permit continuous functioning. Great muscular exertion, for instance, produces large quantities of lactic acid (the acid of sour milk). If this acid were allowed to accumulate in the muscles without being neutralized, it would make the blood less alkaline, and the individual would soon collapse and die. Large amounts of oxygen are required to transform this acid back into muscle sugar. However, the body can take in no more than four liters of oxygen per minute, far less than is needed to accomplish the transformation. The solution is to let the neutralized lactic acid accumulate for a while: the muscles continue to function, though less efficiently. The oxygen debt is then paid after the exercise stops; panting brings enough fresh oxygen into the system to transform the excess acid into glycogen.

The body's blunders

There are many such homeostatic mechanisms in the body, each designed to cope with some challenge. Unfortunately, every response of the body carries its own dangers. "Scarring is supposed to be one of the finest and most effective of the homeostatic mechanisms of healing," points out Dr. Dickinson Richards of Columbia University College of Physicians and Surgeons. "But is it always so? What about scar tissue in rheumatoid arthritis, ending in frozen immobile joints, scar tissue in kidneys, ending in glomerular nephritis, scar tissue in the liver, ending in cirrhosis, and so on through the list? In trying to be homeostatic in one direction, the body finds that it has been most unhomeostatic in another. What about the Wisdom of the Body in all this? Is the body, indeed, so wise? No, one must conclude that it is not. It is stupid, egregiously, calamitously stupid."

The failings and stupidities of the body have always troubled mankind. For most of the years of his existence on earth, man blamed his bodily ills on demons: malignant spirits, spirits of the dead, witches, sorcerers or the evil eye. Today, germs have taken over the demons' role. Illness is still spoken of as if it were a form of possession; it is something one "catches" or "has." The belief that a "bug" causes any given illness has a certain attractive simplicity, because it carries its recommendation for therapy with it: exorcise the bug with drugs.

Actually, few diseases have only one cause. Thousands of people carry within them the microbes of influenza, tuberculosis, staphylococcus infections and many other illnesses, but this single factor does not make them develop the disease. However, inclement weather or starvation or even a family quarrel may provide the trigger that makes the disease flare up. Every illness, no matter what its nature, is usually the consequence of a variety of causes, not just one—and no two people react to any one cause in the same way. Thus disease itself is a failure of homeostasis—a failure to respond appropriately to challenge.

The challenges that confront the body may take many forms. One of the most threatening is that of the unfamiliar microbe. The 18th

DEMONS AND EVIL SPIRITS have been blamed for causing disease in almost every society. This 1862 Japanese woodcut, from a book on the treatment of disease, tells of a samurai warrior afflicted by measles. He is wakened by three girls whom he takes to be the witches who cursed him with the disease. He draws his sword, but stays his hand when they explain that they have the measles too. The picture cards they hold are talismans that were believed to cure the disease.

Century European navigators who first explored the South Pacific and Hawaii found the inhabitants robust and happy, well adapted to their environment. But the explorers' visit changed the picture. The microbes they carried—to which they were immune—spread like wildfire through the Polynesian islands. Practically the entire population of Hawaii came down with measles, and many thousands died. The Westerners brought other infections with them, too: whooping cough, venereal disease, tuberculosis and influenza all struck Hawaii with terrible force. The islands' population had been about 300,000 at the time of Captain Cook's first visit in 1778; by 1860, there were fewer than 37,000 Hawaiians. In precisely the same way, the Great Plagues, the most devastating microbial infections of all, were introduced to Europe from the Orient.

Man today is better able to cope with infectious disease, at least in the industrialized nations. The credit for this is usually given to modern medicine, and especially to the wonder drugs, but in fact their role has been secondary. The major health gains have resulted largely from social measures. Modern sanitary methods have made it possible to prevent the most virulent microbes from ever reaching their human targets. Drinking water is filtered, tested and chlorinated to kill off the germs of intestinal infections. Control of food production and preparation minimizes bacterial contamination. Even vaccination—a method of teaching the body to resist such infectious diseases as smallpox—is as much a social as a medical measure. It is only when these social measures fail to prevent infection that medicine steps in, with its arsenal of drugs.

The lethal power of poverty

The importance of social measures to the health of the Western world can be judged by the situation in the underdeveloped countries, where such measures often have yet to be taken. Because diet in these areas is inadequate, the inhabitants' resistance to infections is very much lowered. In the lands of the have-nots, all the cards are stacked against health. People in India live so close to the subsistence level that only one out of every three Indians born in 1964 can expect to survive to the age of 50; even half a century ago, the life expectancy in the U.S. and Europe was higher than this. Severe malnutrition, multiple infections and infestations by parasites kill nearly 20 per cent of the children of India before they are five, and many of those who survive to adulthood are perpetually tired and weak.

The magnitude of the health problems in these countries defies the imagination. The knowledge that can solve them is available, but until social and economic changes are made, no amount of medical and scientific knowledge can be of much help. Better farming methods must be developed so that people do not die of malnutrition or starvation; good roads must be built to carry all kinds of supplies—from food to vaccine. Sanitary measures must be instituted.

The industrial nations do not have the same environmental problems as the have-nots, but they have others almost as serious. Many of these they have created for themselves. Pollution is an obvious example. Increasingly, it is being recognized that the chemicals that contaminate air and water, and even new drugs, may be serious menaces to health. Another example is obesity. In contrast to the underdeveloped nations, where malnutrition is a threat, overeating has produced a serious health problem in the United States. Life-insurance studies make it clear that obesity itself reduces life expectancy; it apparently plays a significant role in heart disease. The pressures of urban life contribute to the development of chronic disease. Mind and body are inextricably linked, and many of the mental and emotional strains under which Western man lives today find their expression in physical illness.

To a great extent, the manner in which the individual reacts to threats to his health depends on his genetic makeup. But here again environment plays a role. The same genetic traits that would prove burdensome in one kind of environment may be ideally suited to another.

The diseases of the long-lived

The leading threats to life in the United States are, by and large, illnesses which strike hardest at age 50 and beyond: heart disease, cancer, atherosclerosis, etc. These chronic illnesses are almost unknown in the developing countries. Undoubtedly part of the explanation is that people in the new nations die too young to suffer the degenerative diseases of old age. Nevertheless, something in the urban, industrialized way of life seems to encourage such conditions as atherosclerosis, a thickening of the arterial walls; the process begins at such an early age among Americans that it was seen in autopsies of soldiers killed in Korea. When the arteries are narrowed by thick deposits along their walls, the blood flows with difficulty, and the smallest clot may block it entirely. If this interruption of circulation occurs in the blood vessels that feed the heart, the result is a heart attack. If a blood clot develops in the brain, the result is a stroke. Both of these events are common occurrences in the industrialized nations. They are rare in the underdeveloped world; almost every study of old people in these lands has revealed that their arteries have as much resilience as those of American men and women in the prime of life.

One day, without question, medicine will learn how to control atherosclerosis. But when that day arrives some other condition, at present quite rare, will doubtless emerge to become a cause of death. What this next layer of the onion will be no one can foretell. Whatever it is, once

PHLEGMATIC

SANGUINE

MELANCHOLY

CHOLERIC

THE BODY'S CHEMISTRY as a key to health and disease is an old idea, as these medieval pictures illustrate. It was believed that the body had four "humors"—phlegm, blood, black bile and yellow bile—and that good health depended on their correct proportions. They were also thought to affect temperament: the phlegmatic man was "given to sloth"; the sanguine one (from the Latin *sanguis*, "blood") loved "mirth and musick, wine and women"; the melancholy fellow (black bile) was pensive; the choleric man was "all violent."

it is peeled other layers will be waiting beneath it.

Every living thing has a maximum life-span. Man, who sometimes lives past 100, has the longest life-span of all mammals, no matter what their size. He also has the widest range of adaptive capacities. He can make use of almost any substance for food. He can live in almost any climate. No matter what the cause of death may be for any individual, there is no immediate prospect of extending human life much beyond its present limits. Even the replacement of worn-out organs by new ones —a matter of considerable current research interest—can have only a temporary effect. Patching up one area will merely expose deficiencies in another. "Aging," says British physiologist Alex Comfort, "is characteristically an increase in the number and variety of homeostatic faults." When enough body functions fail, the organism dies.

In any event, the chronic diseases seem to be here to stay—at least for the time being. As thousands of invalids can testify, precious little progress has been made in discovering how to treat—let alone prevent —these conditions. But if suffering has not been eliminated, death for most of mankind has certainly been postponed. And as long as man survives, it is at least reasonable to hope that, through further knowledge, he will be able to change the social and cultural conditions that account for the most serious illnesses of our time.

Environment, Health and Mortality

One of the least appreciated influences on disease is environment. Where a man lives and how he lives may have a greater effect on his health—often in unsuspected ways—than the microbes he encounters or the genes he inherits. A laborer in a rock quarry is likely to contract silicosis, a respiratory ailment caused by the dust he inhales. People who live in the tropics are scourged by malaria, a disease seldom encountered in temperate zones. City dwellers almost never get hookworm, a parasitic disease that usually enters the body through the bare feet. Nevertheless, a civilized environment is not always the healthiest one. The Australian aborigines, living in relative isolation in a Stone Age culture, are remarkably free of disease. In fact, it is only in the most advanced societies that civilized man, through the science of modern medicine, begins to approximate the good health the world's least civilized people enjoy as a birthright.

THE CYCLE OF HEALTH
Although the aborigine is one of the world's most primitive men, he is also one of the healthiest— ranking with the U.S. worker and the Swedish businessman. It is the man in transition, such as the Indian farmer or the Nigerian slum dweller, who suffers most: he enjoys neither the simple, healthful life of the savage nor the benefits of the advanced medicine of the industrialized nations

INDIAN FARMER

AMERICAN WORKER

AUSTRALIAN
ABORIGINE

SWEDISH EXECUTIVE

NIGERIAN SLUM DWELLER

17

The Benefits of Isolation

In a few remote corners of the world live men who have been bypassed by modern civilization. Many of these Stone Age people lead remarkably healthy lives. The western Australian aborigines, for example, are as close to nature as any group on earth. They have no medical knowledge. They lead nomadic lives in a parched and hostile land. Their foods are simple.

But these very facts appear to protect them from disease. Their desert surroundings are baked sterile by the sun. They have no dwellings to become fouled by excrement in which germs flourish. Their diet—kangaroo, lizards and emus, nuts, ants and wild yams—is bizarre but balanced. They know little illness and may live to see their great-grandchildren.

AN EXPECTANT MOTHER walks across the desert under a glaring sun. In this artist's rendering—done in the style of aborigine art, with its curious "X-ray" technique—the woman is shown holding a wild yam in one hand; in the other is a bag made of bark, which holds her possessions. When the time comes for the baby to be born, the tribe will halt, but it will be on the move again in a few days. Occasionally aborigine women die in childbirth, but most have easy deliveries. Infancy is one of the most dangerous times for these people: a baby may get an intestinal infection, or die of pneumonia or of an accident. But surviving babies grow fat and healthy in a permissive atmosphere that might appall even a doting American grandmother.

GROOMING FOR MANHOOD, two healthy young boys stalk a fringed lizard and an emu. Although they are not old enough to be entirely self-sufficient, the hunters-to-be help add to the tribal food supply. At the same time, the exercise they get prepares them for the rigorous life of adulthood. There is little malnutrition among the aborigines. Although food is hard to come by, there is almost always enough.

THE END OF CHILDHOOD arrives painfully for aborigine boys. When they are 12 or 13, they are initiated into adulthood. Their bodies are mutilated with a sharpened rock, and ceremonial scars are cut across their chests. The rough gashes are packed with clay so they will leave decorative scars after healing. Though disinfectants are unknown, the natural sterility of the desert helps minimize infection. Now they must take their places as adult members of the tribe. When a tribesman does get too sick to keep up with the tribe, he is left to starve.

OUT HUNTING, an aborigine man, having already speared a large kangaroo, takes aim with his boomerang on a smaller specimen. Helping him in the chase is a half-wild dog. The ceaseless search for food and water keeps the tribe forever on the move, and this may contribute to its healthy state.

DEATH AND THE "DREAM TIME" may not come for more than 80 years, though most aborigines die by age 65. If the spirits have been good, if water and food have been plentiful and accidents few, if a member of another family has not been offended and sought revenge through magic so potent the offender loses the will to live—then the aborigine can count on a life as full of years as any civilized man's. When he is dead, the mystic symbols that are on his churinga, or totem, may be painted on his body. Aborigines believe in an afterlife and reincarnation: at death, the soul enters the "dream time," to rest until its rebirth in another person.

19

The Cost of Cleanliness

The farmers of rural India, like hundreds of millions of people in Asia, Africa and South America, are culturally a long step ahead of the aborigines. They wear clothes, live in houses, have a complex social organization and till their fields. Unlike the aborigines, who know nothing of sanitation, the Indians have an almost obsessive drive to be clean. But they stable their oxen in their houses. They constantly wash their clothes and their bodies—but they do it in the same wells that supply them with drinking water. They raise their own food—but it is often woefully lacking in proteins and vitamins. Subject to a host of contagious diseases, rural Indians actually have a life-span shorter than that of the aborigines.

SPREADING DISEASE, an Indian mother wipes the eyes of her baby with the tip of her shawl. The flies around her may carry trachoma, which can cause blindness. The shawl may have been contaminated by the flies, or she may have used it to wipe the eyes of another child already infected. Thus, through attempts at cleanliness, she may actually spread contagion. Her other children have distended stomachs as a result of malnutrition. When Indian children are weaned, they are fed a starchy gruel. This diet can cause kwashiorkor, a protein-deficiency disease that lowers resistance to contagious diseases.

CONTAMINATING WATER, Indian women rinse dirty jugs in the same supply they use for drinking. Rural Indians have no plumbing or sewage systems, and because they believe that odor causes disease they even shun outhouses, using open fields instead. Rain falling on the fouled fields seeps into the ground, eventually reaching village wells, and bearing with it the microbes of cholera, typhoid and other diseases. In the background a housewife cooks over a fire of dried cow dung. Cows are sacred, and their dung is thought to be imbued with purifying and medicinal powers: it is sometimes rubbed in wounds as a poultice. In the process, it spreads tetanus, estimated to rank fourth among the killing diseases in India.

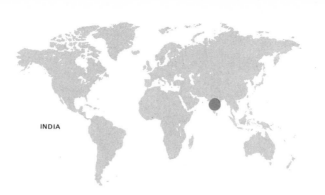

PRIMITIVE PLOWING and undernourished oxen limit the size and quality of Indian crops and—along with inferior seed strains, poor soil and overpopulation—contribute to malnutrition and its attendant ills. In the foreground a child adds his weight to the harrow. The man at the bottom chops grass for cattle fodder with a hand-turned blade.

LIVING WITH ANIMALS under the same roof, an Indian family prepares for the evening meal. The man lying on the couch has tuberculosis; the sick in rural India commonly stay with their families until the disease reaches an advanced state. During the rainy season, mortality rates increase. The heavy rains help to contaminate wells and rivers, and provide breeding grounds for mosquitoes. A baby born during this season has so little chance for survival that there is often a "birthday" celebration if he lives 40 days.

THE BURDENS OF AGE in India include lingering diseases such as leprosy and tuberculosis—and loneliness: by the time a man is 60, more than half his contemporaries are dead. Too old to work, the handful of surviving oldsters gather under the pipal tree in the village to gossip and reminisce about lives devoted almost entirely to keeping alive.

In Search of the Good Life

Nigeria is one of the world's newest nations, striving to leap into the 20th Century virtually overnight. Its capital, Lagos, like many cities in emerging nations, reflects this difficult transition. The downtown section is filled with modern buildings, automobiles, government officials and healthy white-collar workers.

But surrounding this hub are festering slums. "The reason there aren't more flies," one visitor has said, "is that they couldn't stand the stench." Crowded into the mud huts and dirt alleys are people who have come from the bush seeking a better life. Instead they find squalor, disease, ignorance that rates the witch doctor on a par with the local clinic, and an air of all-pervading failure and futility.

DANGEROUSLY OVERCROWDED, a family of 11 cram into their one-room hut. The woman with the baby is likely to be tubercular, as are other members of the family. Death visits most often during the first four years of life, when, in addition to the normal diseases of childhood, such as measles and mumps, youngsters are also subject to pneumonia, malaria, typhoid and gastrointestinal ailments. Of every 10 babies born, three die in their first year; half are dead by age five.

STOLEN VITAMINS, in the form of fruit snatched from a market basket, may be this young boy's salvation. Superstition has it that fresh fruit and eggs are bad for children and pregnant women. But children, driven by hunger, often steal the vitamin-rich food they need.

FILTHY MARKETS are the chief source of food for Lagotian slum dwellers. Here, swarming with insects and dispensed by peddlers who are often diseased, snails, yams and cooking oil —foods of questionable nutritional value— may be bought at inflationary prices. Wild fruits and nuts, laboriously gathered by townspeople on forays into the surrounding jungle, are also available. Meat is in very short supply, and the adults eat what little there is instead of giving it to the children, who need it for proper growth. Refrigeration is rare, and spoilage runs high.

NIGERIA

SEEKING A LIVING, a young Lagotian works as a messenger. His bicycle, probably purchased with the meager savings of years, will not guarantee him a steady income, or even one he can hope to live on. To provide the bare minimum amount of food his family requires, he may have to consign his children to the streets to beg for alms.

THE INROADS OF DISEASE leave few elderly people. So prevalent are meningitis, typhoid fever, influenza and tuberculosis that only three persons out of 10 live to mark their 25th birthday. Even at that age, people often appear to be twice their years—and physically they may be. Thus, at age 30 or so, a typical slum-dwelling Lagotian is rarely equal to the competition for what few jobs are available. And then the death watch begins. He may go into the streets and beg, but in Lagos alms are rare. Or he may stay at home, crowded into a corner of his hut by a new generation of grandchildren. Under such conditions, mental breakdown frequently becomes the only form of escape and, like the man in the background, he may run amok or kill himself.

The Penalties of the Good Life

In the industrialized nations live the people who may benefit most from the medical advances of this century: the wage earners of industrial society. For the most part well off, they live in cities—e.g., Chicago, Cleveland, Detroit—which have adequate sanitary and medical facilities.

But there is a paradox in this. They are well nourished, but they overeat.

They escape some afflictions, only to get others: cancer, diabetes and heart diseases have simply replaced most of the infectious diseases. Progress has eased working conditions and lengthened life. But it has also taken its toll in the form of illnesses such as ulcers, born of the strains of an increasingly specialized and competitive as well as fast-changing society.

Bernard Perlin

IN A HYGIENIC HOSPITAL typical of those in an industrialized city, a mother can be seen through the window holding her newborn baby, while outside another mother bottle-feeds her child. The hazards of infancy have been so reduced that the first-year death rate is only 25 out of 1,000 births.

THE GROWING YEARS are generally healthy ones. The effects of measles and chicken pox are minimal and seldom cause any worse problems than a few days away from school. There is plenty of play and time to read. Through the late teens, exercise and diet-conscious mothers keep bodies in trim. But after high school, with marriage and, often, a physically undemanding job, the seeds of future problems begin to germinate. An evening a week of bowling replaces regular gym classes, beer replaces milk—and the waist begins to thicken.

INDUSTRIAL AMERICA

GOOD WORKING CONDITIONS prevail in most factories. They are well-lighted. On-the-job safety is emphasized. Most big companies maintain clinics staffed by full-time physicians. And an increasing number of corporations employ psychologists, who help workers with emotional problems. Off the job, medical insurance often helps provide workers and their families with medical care.

THE PRICE OF MEDICAL PROGRESS is ultimately exacted in the form of diseases virtually unknown outside of mature industrial societies. These overweight factory hands, eating lunches heavy in fats, have no worries about undernutrition. On the contrary, they are raising their cholesterol intake to dangerous levels, and thus may be increasing their chances of contracting heart disease. Their work can keep them sedentary during the day; television and the automobile do the same during their leisure hours. But they are far from serene, a fact that creates additional health hazards. Concerned about bills and about job security, they are subject to anxiety, which can lead to such afflictions as spastic colitis and peptic ulcers.

THE "GOLDEN YEARS" are a time for relaxation. With an income from pension plans and Social Security, a retired worker often has a chance to indulge in hobbies that he never before had time for. But these are also the years of the chronic diseases of the aged: atherosclerosis, diabetes, emphysema. Furthermore, the retired man, after working so hard and long for his rest, may find himself unprepared for leisure. Boredom may exact a toll in life: in the years between 65 and 70, the death rate among retired men is higher than for those who continue to work.

The Healthiest People

In prosperous Sweden poverty is virtually unknown, and the best medical care is available to all. The healthiest people in this healthy land are those of the professional class, who may have the best health record in the world. These people are cared for, quite literally, from birth until death, sheltered in clean homes, treated in the most up-to-date hospitals.

As a result, the average life expectancy in Sweden is the world's highest—71.6 years for men, 75.4 for women.

Nevertheless, the maximum age a Swede can hope to reach is no higher than that among the aborigines. Old age is the one serious affliction that falls with equal weight on both civilized and primitive man—and even the greatest doctors cannot cure it.

FAT AND HEALTHY, a week-old Swedish baby naps in his hospital bassinet. In Sweden only about 15 of every 1,000 babies die during the first year, 40 per cent fewer than in the U.S., and often the cause of death is accident, not disease. Whether the baby is born at home or in a hospital, most of the cost is borne by the Government and the rest usually comes from voluntary medical insurance.

THE EARLY YEARS in Sweden are a time of carefully controlled health measures. Government-sponsored medicine makes available regular medical care for youngsters at little or no expense to their families. In school they get periodic physical examinations; at home they are fed carefully balanced meals. In the cities, parks and playgrounds are found everywhere. Yet the seeds of trouble are sown in these years. Although growing children are physically pampered, they are taught to suppress emotion, rigorously to obey their parents without question, and to get along with their brothers and sisters with no fuss. Many psychologists believe that this suppression becomes an important factor in the emotional problems of later years.

SWEDEN

AS ADOLESCENTS, young Swedes are expected to assume adult responsibilities by parents who believe that decision-making leads to self-reliance. The youngsters receive little real guidance in such matters as smoking, drinking and sex; instead, they must find their own way—often before they are ready, some psychologists feel. The result is a growing sense of insecurity. Although sports-loving Swedish youngsters are often outwardly gay and self-reliant, they may have serious emotional problems. Many Swedish colleges actually post signs offering help to despondent students.

AT THE PEAK OF HIS CAREER, a Swedish executive faces an uncertain future so far as his health is concerned. With executives everywhere he shares certain problems: girth-thickening business lunches, chain-smoking, the social necessity (and perhaps emotional need) for drink and, most of all, worry—the kind that often produces ulcers. He may have enjoyed a half century of excellent health, but the healthy years are fast ticking away. Soon he will be menaced—if he is not already—by the chronic diseases such as atherosclerosis and cancer.

THE QUIET TIME of life is a rich one for most retired Swedes. Full retirement benefits are paid at age 63, regardless of economic status. Partly because the labor force is smaller than in many industrial nations, there is little discrimination against the aged in hiring. One man who had his fill of leisure returned to work for the post office—at 94.

27

The Distribution of Disease

The ties between environment and disease are dramatically illustrated by the maps on these pages. The maps, which show the relative severity of six types of disease, make it clear that where a man lives may be the greatest influence on his health. Americans, for example, are unlikely to die of infectious, digestive or respiratory diseases—but these are killers in Africa, South America and Asia.

Some kinds of disease become common in more civilized areas simply by a process of elimination. Thus, childhood diseases assume greater relative importance in the U.S. than in parts of Africa because African children die early of other ailments.

The importance of environment is exemplified by Ceylon. This island, only 20 miles off the Indian coast, has its own economics, geography, culture—and its own health statistics, markedly different from India's.

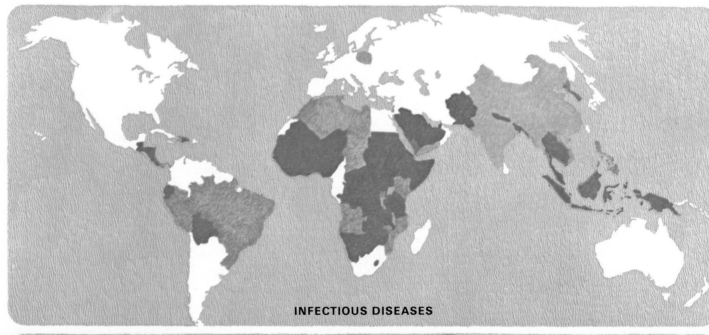

INFECTIOUS DISEASES

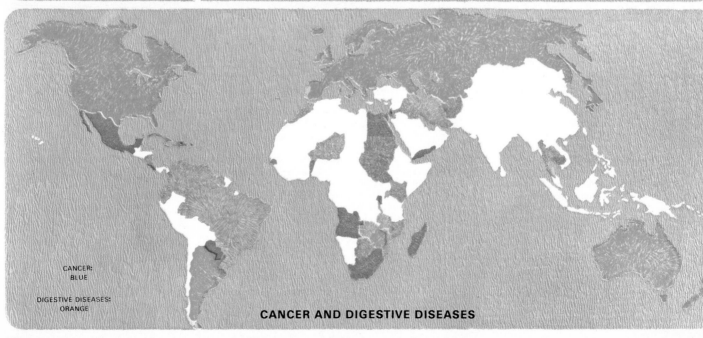

CANCER:
BLUE

DIGESTIVE DISEASES:
ORANGE

CANCER AND DIGESTIVE DISEASES

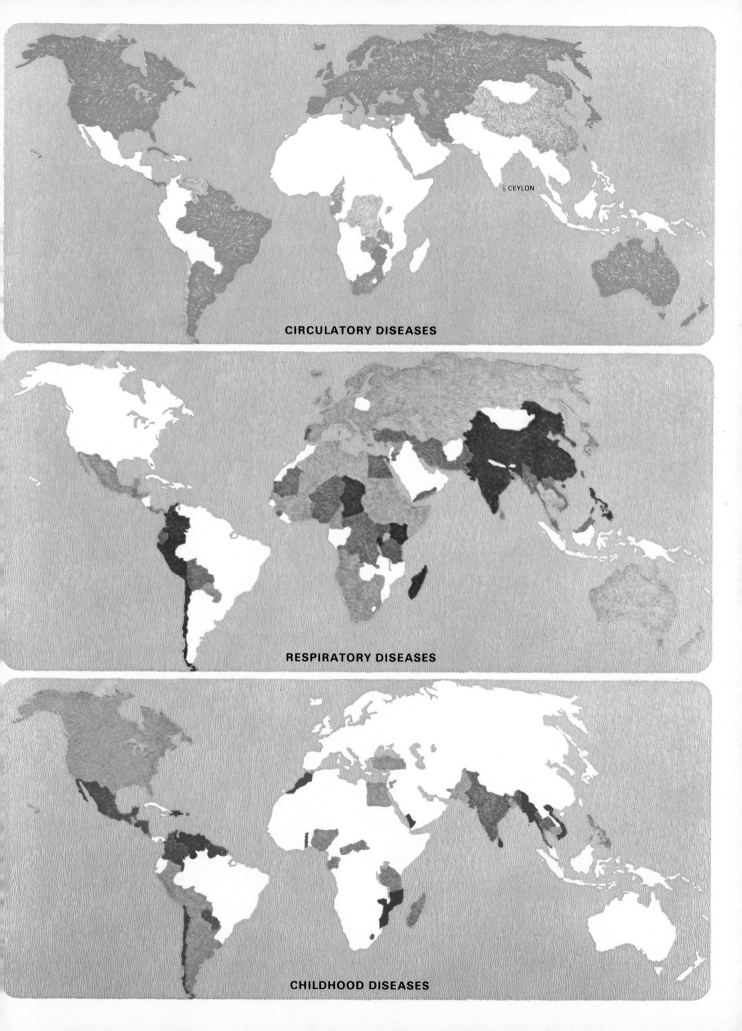

CIRCULATORY DISEASES

CEYLON

RESPIRATORY DISEASES

CHILDHOOD DISEASES

2
The Great
Plagues

DURING THE 14TH CENTURY, traders from Mediterranean and Black Sea ports made their way to China, bringing back precious silks and furs. Returning from such a trip in 1343, a group of Genoese merchants reportedly fled in terror from a band of Tartars and took refuge in the walled trading post of Caffa in the Crimea. The Tartars promptly besieged the town. For three years neither side made any headway until one day the Tartars stopped catapulting mere rocks and stones over Caffa's walls, and began hurling in bodies—the corpses of their own men who had died of bubonic plague.

With this experiment in bacteriological warfare, the Tartars touched off the worst pandemic in the history of mankind. As the plague-ridden bodies landed behind the walls of Caffa, the whole town became infected. Then suddenly the besiegers disappeared, probably in panic at their own mounting losses from the plague. The Genoese survivors at once ran to their ships and sailed away. Many of them died on shipboard, but the rest landed in Constantinople, Genoa, Venice and other ports, where they infected families and friends.

And so the Black Death came to Europe. As it had spread from Asia to the Crimea, so it spread northward and westward from the Mediterranean ports to the interior, from Italy and Greece to France, Spain and England. It left no hamlet untouched, increasing in ferocity until in 1348 two thirds of the population of Europe was afflicted. During the eight years of the pandemic, at least half of the sick died—an almost incredible total of 25 million people. There was no place to hide: even those who fled to sea discovered the plague as a stowaway on their ships.

The chronicle of an Irish friar, John Clyn, gives some idea of the prevailing desolation and despair. "That pestilence," he wrote, "deprived of human inhabitants villages and cities, and castles and towns, so that there was scarcely found a man to dwell therein. Whosoever touched the sick or dead was immediately infected and died, and the penitent and the confessor were carried together to the grave. Many died of boils and abscesses, others frantic with pain in their head, and others spitting blood. I, waiting for death till it come, have reduced these things to writing. . . ." A few lines below on Clyn's manuscript is the copyist's entry: "Here, it seems, the author died."

From earliest times to the present, microbial infection has posed a major threat to the health of civilized man. The bubonic plague—even more than such later "plagues" as cholera, smallpox, yellow fever and influenza—remains the outstanding example of the infectious disease which sweeps in from abroad to ravage entire populations that have had no previous exposure to it.

The bubonic plague was known as far back as Biblical times, when it attacked the Philistines through their seaports. The first great bubonic

PLAGUE-STRUCK NAPLES
The chaos and terror that plague brought to 17th Century Naples are dramatically portrayed in this painting by Micco Spadaro, an eyewitness to the epidemic in 1656. The death rate was so enormous that a burial ritual was initiated. *Apparitori,* or summoners, would walk the streets ringing bells—the signal for residents to bring out their dead to be buried.

pandemic, the Plague of Justinian in the Sixth Century, also broke out during a period of increased international trade. Its catastrophic effect on the Roman world played a large role in ushering in the Dark Ages.

After the plague had swept Europe in the 14th Century, it remained smoldering for 300 years, flaring up whenever susceptible persons were crowded together. More and more it became an urban disease with major seaports and commercial centers suffering repeated outbreaks.

The horrors of '65

These epidemics reached a climax in London with the Great Plague of 1665. In September of that year, the city of London's weekly Bills of Mortality showed that more than 30,000 persons died. But even these bills did not tell the whole story. People went to great lengths to hide new cases as long as possible for fear of being shut up in their own homes. There was only one "pest-house," or hospital, in the entire city, so whenever it was learned that someone had come down with the plague officials simply locked up that person and everyone else who had associated with him—parents, children, servants and visitors alike. The door of the house was painted with a large red cross, topped by the words "Lord have mercy on us," and a watchman stood guard day and night until four weeks after everybody inside had been pronounced healthy. For most of the sick, the "dead-cart" was the only way out.

To avoid being imprisoned in their houses, large numbers of families fled London as soon as they knew one of their members had the plague. Others managed to escape their branded houses while the watchman's back was turned, or by overpowering him. And so they spread the disease, first to nearby towns, and finally throughout England.

In London itself, all commerce, all traffic came to a halt. People were afraid to approach one another. Even the busy dealers in charms and amulets to ward off the plague disappeared from the streets, and so did the swarms of quack doctors who sold worthless potions and pills. Nor were the reputable physicians of the day able to stop the disease. The buboes, or swellings, which gave the plague its name appeared generally under the armpits or in the groin; the physicians used hot poultices, burning caustic and knives in an effort to make the swellings break and run, believing that if this happened the patient might be saved. For the most part they failed. Soon they stopped visiting infected houses—either from fear or hopelessness, or because they too had died. Finally, in the autumn of 1666, the plague retreated from London. After 1720, except for isolated outbreaks, it disappeared from Western Europe as well.

Before it subsided, however, the plague had profound effects on Europe's social structure. It helped to shatter the feudal system by putting a new price on the labor supply that remained. It also changed age-old

FLEEING THE PLAGUE, wealthy Londoners took to the country at every major outbreak, leaving the city's poor to the mercies of pestilence, famine and lawlessness. But as this woodcut of the 1630 plague makes plain, the specters of death rode the carriages of the rich and moved freely among their unwilling country hosts regardless of wealth or rank.

attitudes toward disease. Until then people had believed that sickness was a sign of God's punishment, but the plague's indiscriminate slaughter of all in its path, saint and sinner alike, made it clear that something more secular was involved. The first hazy notions of contagion appeared. "Poisonous vapors," "putrid fumes" and "corrupted and pestilential air" began to be blamed for disease, rather than sin or lack of faith. Even though the early attempts at quarantine proved ineffectual, the ground was laid for the beginning of public sanitation.

As has been amply demonstrated since then, a few isolated cases of plague do not make an epidemic, nor does an epidemic in one area necessarily turn into a widespread pandemic. It is now known that bubonic plague is spread by infected rats that live in close contact with man and pass the infection on to him through the bite of their fleas. Occasionally the disease has taken the form of a highly contagious pneumonia—pneumonic plague—which is transmitted directly from man to man in droplets coughed out by its victims. Both kinds are caused by the same bacillus, *Pasteurella pestis,* which was not actually identified until 1894. This organism still thrives among wild rodents in various parts of the world: the major permanent reservoir of infection exists in the steppes of Central Asia, where marmots and gophers carry it throughout their lives. The danger occurs when these creatures spread the plague to domesticated rats, particularly to black rats, the most home-loving of all.

The plague's inability to maintain a foothold in Europe after 1720 has been traced mainly to the disappearance of the black rat. This creature was driven out partly by gradual improvements in housing and partly by another rat, the hardier brown rat, which swarmed across the Volga from eastern Russia in 1727 and spread rapidly by land and sea. Known as "sewer rats," these animals are the ones still commonly seen in Europe and the U.S. As their name implies, they tend to live in sewers or to wander about, keeping away from human beings. Furthermore, the kind of flea they carry is far less effective than that of the black rat in transmitting the plague to man.

The Manchurian marmots

Under certain conditions, however, the plague has become epidemic even in modern times. Around 1910, for example, a change in ladies' fashions created a sudden demand for the fur of the Manchurian marmot, which was ideal for making imitation sable and sealskin. This led thousands of inexperienced Chinese hunters to hunt for these wild rodents in an area where rodent plague was endemic. Until then this job had been left to professional Manchurian hunters, who followed an ancient tradition that sick marmots were to be avoided at all costs. The Chinese hunters trapped every animal within reach—and since

BURIAL BY NIGHT, without ceremony, was the lot of London plague victims in 1665. When the graveyards were filled, bodies were simply heaped on "dead-carts" and thrown into huge "plague-pits." In this engraving of the period, both men are smoking pipes to ward off contagion. The man at right drags corpses off the cart with a hook to avoid touching them.

healthy marmots make difficult targets, the sickest ones proved the easiest prey. It was not long before several of the hunters came down with the plague, and in crowded, ill-ventilated Manchurian inns they soon transmitted it in pneumonic form to others. Thus began an epidemic which took 60,000 lives in Manchuria and China in 1910 and 1911.

Although this was the last great plague epidemic, the threat lingers on. Surprisingly, the U.S. today has a potentially dangerous reservoir of rodent plague, which may owe its existence to the carelessness of the state of California at the turn of the century. When a few cases of plague were discovered in San Francisco's Chinatown in 1900, the federal Government immediately sent an official with instructions to wipe out the disease. But Californians became so indignant at the suggestion that there was bubonic plague in their state that they publicly assaulted the investigator. Only the threat of a federal quarantine, which would have stopped all people and goods from crossing the state line, forced the authorities to begin setting out poisoned rat food and taking other measures. By that time, however, the rats had infected ground squirrels, that carried it through the state. In 1919, 14 cases of plague occurred in Oakland; in 1924, 30 persons died of it in Los Angeles. Slowly the ground-squirrel infection spread to 15 of the Western states. Pockets of plague have since been discovered in squirrels, chipmunks, prairie dogs, wood rats and harvest mice as far east as Kansas. Epidemiologists are keeping careful watch on these animals, particularly the smallest and least conspicuous of them, the field mice, which often share human habitations with domestic rats during winter months and may pass on their infected fleas to them.

Cleaning up the plague

Should any cases of human plague break out today, the world is far better equipped to deal with them than ever before. Fleas can be exterminated; vaccines give some hope of protection. And if used early enough, antibiotics such as streptomycin can cure both bubonic and pneumonic forms of the plague. Even if such weapons did not exist, experience has shown that epidemics of plague are unlikely to develop in countries with a high level of sanitation. Neither in England, nor in Australia, nor in the U.S., where the plague has made several appearances in this century, has it shown any tendency to spread widely among humans. But it still takes its annual toll in countries with more crowding and less hygiene: in 1962, for example, nearly 700 persons died of plague in India, and 326 died in Ecuador.

While the U.S. has been spared major epidemics of the plague, it has had devastating outbreaks of other diseases. Probably the most dramatic was yellow fever, or yellow jack, which in the 18th Century raged

A CHOLERA COSTUME, this attire appeared in a Viennese cartoon during a serious cholera outbreak in the 19th Century. It simply exaggerated the many desperate notions people had about how the disease was transmitted and how best to ward it off: outsized shoes to avoid contamination from the ground, bottles of medicine in a basket, bags of aromatic herbs to overcome toxic vapors, a windmill to dispel evil air. Even the lady's dog wore shoes and carried a syringe.

through the country in 35 separate epidemics. Brought in by ship from the West Indies, yellow fever struck again and again during the summer months, culminating in the disastrous Philadelphia epidemic of 1793.

Like London's great bubonic plague a century earlier, Philadelphia's yellow jack produced general panic. Thousands of people fled the city, and notices were posted on all infected houses. Those who could not get away—including virtually all the city's poor—sought protection by breathing through cloth masks soaked in garlic juice, vinegar or camphor, or by equally ineffective methods. When the disease struck, it killed at least one in five of those who contracted it, after high fever, jaundice (the yellow skin that gave the illness its name), hiccuping and vomiting of blood. Nearly all of the 24,000 persons who remained in Philadelphia were afflicted. Almost 5,000 people died.

Those who believed that the fever was contagious blamed contaminated articles. They fumigated or burned every bit of "infected" bedding and clothing they could find, with no effect on the spread of the disease. However, America's leading physician at the time, Dr. Benjamin Rush, denied that contagion was a major cause of yellow jack. He believed all fevers were forms of the same "primary disease in the sanguiferous system," and thus not catching. The epidemic, Dr. Rush claimed, was caused by noxious "exhalations" from a pile of coffee that had rotted on a wharf, and from such other sources as rotten cabbage, bilge water, duck ponds, musty old books and privies. To cure patients he prescribed a frightening course of treatment which he applied with vigor: stiff purges of jalap and calomel, bloodlettings, ipecac to produce vomiting, and buckets of cold water thrown on the patient frequently to reduce fever. This probably finished off some patients, weakening them just when they needed all their strength, and it nearly finished off Dr. Rush as well. Hundreds of friends and neighbors begged for his personal help, and he continued his heroic, though misguided, efforts until he finally collapsed from exhaustion and the fever. It was not until more than a century later that yellow fever was identified as a virus-caused disease transmitted by the mosquito *Aëdes aegypti*.

Cholera: the deadly immigrant

Cholera, the swiftest-striking of all the great plagues, also came from abroad, but it did not reach the U.S. until the great waves of immigrants arrived in the 19th Century. Many of these people had contracted the disease in seaports just before boarding their ships, for a serious epidemic of Asiatic cholera was then raging in Europe. The cholera bacterium was passed from passenger to passenger by direct contact and through contaminated food and water, causing sudden vomiting, diarrhea and death. In this way cholera brought by immigrants swept across the U.S.

TRAILS OF DEATH mark the spread of cholera from India during the 19th Century. At the time, most people blamed the east wind for carrying the disease. Actually, as the map below indicates, cholera spread along the main routes of trade and migration, moving from Asia to Europe and from there to the Americas in successive waves. The 1848 epidemic rode the emigrant ships from Europe, then traveled up the Mississippi in time to infect the Forty-niners, who carried it to California along with their gold fever.

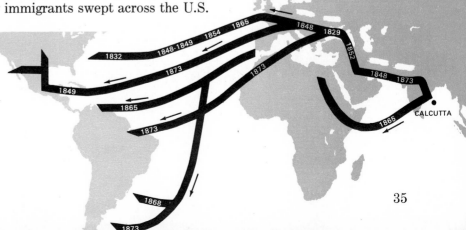

35

in 1832, 1849, 1866 and again in 1873, ravaging great areas along the Atlantic seaboard and reaching from the Gulf of Mexico to the Great Lakes and the West Coast. Five years after the last epidemic the federal Government finally instituted a nationwide system of offshore quarantine to check incoming ships for cholera, and for yellow fever and smallpox as well. Thanks to this innovation, and to advances in sanitation and vaccination, the U.S. has seen relatively little of these three diseases since.

The mysterious beginnings

Not surprisingly, foreigners have always received more than their share of blame for the spread of disease—not only cholera and yellow fever, but various others as well. In ancient folklore, the "plague-woman" always came from some other village. Syphilis, one of the most prevalent diseases of the 16th through 20th Centuries, was called the "Neapolitan" sickness by the French—and the "French" sickness by the Italians. Actually no one knows where it came from, and no one wants to take the credit. To this day some historians maintain that syphilis had long been known in Europe, while others believe Spanish conquistadors brought it back from the Americas.

In fact, mystery surrounds not only the origin of many diseases, but also the ways they develop and the reasons they wane. It is not definitely known, for instance, why leprosy, which was epidemic in Europe for hundreds of years, disappeared after the 16th Century. Nor is there any explanation for the "sweat," the terrible sickness that visited England periodically between 1485 and 1551 and then vanished without a trace. Spreading with lightning speed, it produced intense sweating and death in a matter of hours for nearly all who became obviously ill. It cannot be identified with any disease we know today, although some regard it as a more acute form of one of our virus diseases.

Some diseases have erupted when men moved into new territory: in the U.S., for example, conditions ideal for the spread of malaria existed when the American pioneers settled in the Mississippi and Ohio Valleys, where the *Anopheles* mosquito lived. As more and more settlers arrived, malaria burst out in an epidemic that reached as far north as Minneapolis and Montreal, killing thousands in its path.

Regardless of where they came from or how they spread, most of the major infectious diseases of history have had one characteristic in common: they have done their greatest damage among populations which were suddenly exposed to them for the first time. The inhabitants of 18th Century England, where smallpox was common, considered it a childhood disease. And in fact it was: one out of three English children died of it before his third birthday. Many others were blinded by it, and most were pockmarked for life—but those who survived were immune to

MALARIA'S CONQUEROR and the mosquito he defeated are affectionately caricatured in a 1908 cartoon published by a newspaper in the British colony of Mauritius. The colony's hero was Sir Ronald Ross, a British Army surgeon, who had proved nine years earlier that malaria was transmitted by the bite of the *Anopheles* mosquito, and not by *mal aria* (Italian for "bad air"). Invited to Mauritius in the Indian Ocean, where malaria had spread with increasing ferocity for 40 years, Ross ordered the mosquito-breeding swamps to be drained, and thus halted the epidemic.

smallpox forever. The Indians of the New World, on the other hand, had never been exposed to the disease, and were particularly vulnerable to it. Shortly after Cortez arrived in Mexico in 1520, smallpox ravaged the Indians there, killing at least half of them, children and adults alike, and so demoralizing the rest that it hastened their defeat. When the English came to fight the Indians of North America a century later, they did not hesitate to take advantage of this susceptibility. By giving away contaminated blankets, they willfully spread smallpox among their foes, while rejoicing that the Lord had sent His "avenging angels to destroy the heathen."

The Europeans soon lost their advantage, however. In the New World, their way of life changed sufficiently to prevent constant exposure to smallpox. The scattered settlements in which they lived had little contact with one another. While they remained isolated, the colonists stayed generally healthy; smallpox infection was often unknown for a whole generation. But meanwhile a large nonimmune population grew up. As a result, whenever a ship brought fresh infections from Europe, smallpox, as well as measles, struck with ferocity. Throughout the 17th Century, smallpox remained the major epidemic disease in the colonies.

The colonists knew of no way to protect themselves from the disease. But in 1716 Lady Mary Montagu, the wife of the British Ambassador to Turkey, wrote to friends in England about the inoculation parties she had witnessed in Constantinople. The Turkish method was to make a small wound in the arm, insert a few drops of smallpox pus in it and tie a walnut shell over the infected area. This produced a true case of smallpox, as contagious as any other, but mild enough so that 98 per cent of those inoculated recovered from it. Soon similar inoculation parties were held in England, with friends taking the treatment at the same time so they could be isolated together. But the inoculations never became popular because there was real danger involved.

Inoculation arrives in America

About the same time Lady Montagu brought them to England, news of the Turkish inoculations reached Cotton Mather in Boston. The famed Puritan minister had learned from a Negro slave that similar immunizations were common in Africa. So in 1721, when another severe epidemic of smallpox broke out in Boston, Mather wrote a treatise on the disease and suggested inoculation. The doctors of his day laughed at the idea— all except one, Dr. Zabdiel Boylston, who proceeded to inoculate one of his sons successfully with live smallpox virus. This daring act touched off a war of pamphlets and so enraged his fellow citizens that Boylston was mobbed and called before the city's selectmen to justify his stand. Clergymen denounced the new practice as a sinful interference with the

VACCINATION OF A BOY by Dr. Edward Jenner marked his discovery of a smallpox preventive, and catapulted him from the obscurity of a rural British practice into international fame. The sculpture above commemorates the day in 1796 when Jenner took cowpox pus from the sore on a milkmaid's hand and smeared it on scratches on a healthy boy's arm, and found a safe method of immunization against the long-feared disease.

course of nature. A homemade bomb was thrown into Mather's home along with a message reading, "Cotton Mather: you Dog, Damn you, I'll inoculate you with this, and a Pox to you!" Nevertheless, 286 bold Bostonians had themselves inoculated. More than half of Boston fell ill with smallpox, and the mortality rate was 15 per cent. But of those who had been inoculated, only six persons died, the expected 2 per cent. Despite continuing opposition from officials who thought it unethical or illegal, inoculation slowly gained in favor. In 1792, when smallpox struck Boston again, more than 8,000 persons volunteered for inoculations.

Four years later, a far safer method of producing immunity was discovered in England. At that time Edward Jenner transferred cowpox from the sore on a milkmaid's hand by scratching it into a young boy's arm—and two months later proved him immune to human smallpox. Jenner's principle, called vaccination, from the Latin *vacca*, for cow, used the live viruses of a milder, related disease to set up a defense mechanism in the human body against later exposure to a deadlier organism. As Jenner's successors found out, other infections such as polio, yellow fever and diphtheria can also be prevented by vaccines containing infectious agents in an attenuated or killed form. Thus, for a long list of mankind's most dreaded diseases, artificial immunity was finally substituted for the natural immunity our ancestors gained at such great cost.

Intermediaries of Disease

The parasitic agents which cause many of man's deadliest ailments are themselves living things whose life patterns are often exceedingly complicated. The protozoon which causes malaria, for example, must dwell in man during one part of its development and in the body of a special kind of mosquito during another. Diseases of this type are referred to as "vector-borne" (from the Latin *vehere*, "to carry"), because they are usually carried from host to host by another creature, often an insect. Without man to serve as a host, some of these diseases would cease to exist. In others, man serves only as an occasional, accidental stopping place. In either case, the key to control of vector-borne diseases lies in breaking the complicated life cycle of the organisms which cause them. Such control often requires a careful strategy that may involve an attack on the vector and the animal host—as well as treatment of the disease in man.

MEALTIME FOR MOSQUITOES

Feeding *Anopheles* mosquitoes on his own blood *(opposite)* is a necessary chore for a scientist at the WHO Experimental Malaria Station in Monticelli, Italy. This vector of malaria, though fed mostly on the blood of guinea pigs, accepts such food only after being fed human blood. The Monticelli station was opened after malaria reached epidemic proportions in Italy after World War II.

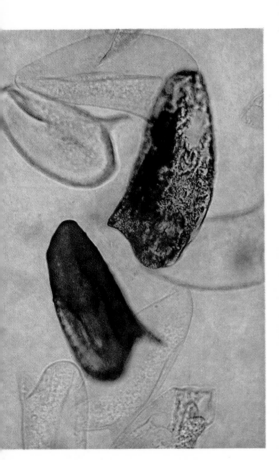

EGGS IN THE HUMAN HOST

Eggs of the parasite *Schistosoma mansoni* *(above)* are found in the lower intestine. Eject-ed with body wastes, the eggs hatch in water and become free-swimming embryos. Within the next eight hours they must find a suitable freshwater snail to survive in, or they will die.

THE INTERMEDIATE HOST

Embryos seek out only certain species of fresh-water snails—in South America and the West Indies, the *Australorbis glabratus* shown here. Entering the snail's body, the embryos settle down and multiply, eventually metamorphos-ing into a new form—tiny, fork-tailed larvae.

Worm's Cycle: Man to Snail to Man

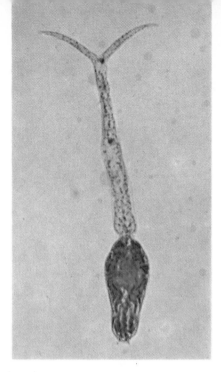

PENETRATING PARASITE

After leaving its snail host, a larva swims until it dies—or comes in contact with its chief victim, man. Penetrating the skin headfirst, the larva sheds its tail and enters the bloodstream.

The small parasitic worms known as schistosomes threaten more than 100 million people in the warmer parts of the world. Persons infested with the parasites develop schistosomiasis, a painful and occasionally fatal disease that damages many organs. The ailment is prevalent in areas where people work in or drink polluted water—usually from rice paddies, streams or ponds contaminated with human sewage.

Unlike many human diseases in which animals play a part, certain forms of schistosomiasis involve no warm-blooded host other than man. Freshwater snails serve as an essential intermediate host. Schistosome eggs hatch into embryos in water,

metamorphose to larvae in the snail, then metamorphose again from larvae to adults in man. As the worms mature, they perform a sort of Cook's tour of the circulatory system, in the process maturing, meeting and mating with other worms, and damaging the blood vessels of their host, often seriously. In many underdeveloped countries with poor sanitation, irrigation ditches are a favorite haunt of the snails that are an essential link in the chain of infection. Thus, ironically, the expansion of irrigation—often vitally necessary if the people are to secure a diet adequate to maintain health—can at the same time undermine their well-being by spreading the parasitic schistosomes.

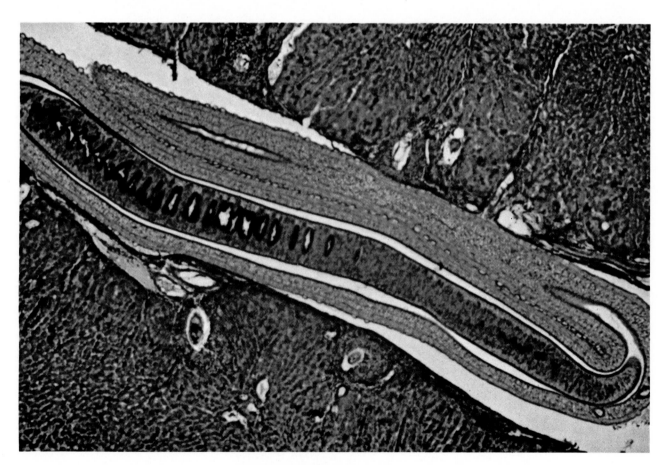

A FATEFUL MEETING

Adult *Schistosoma mansoni* worms, with the inch-long female enfolded in the male, are shown in this cross section of a blood vessel in the human liver. Males act as capsules that transport the females into intestinal blood vessels, where they lay their eggs to begin the cycle anew. On their way through the body, the worms cause abscesses and internal bleeding.

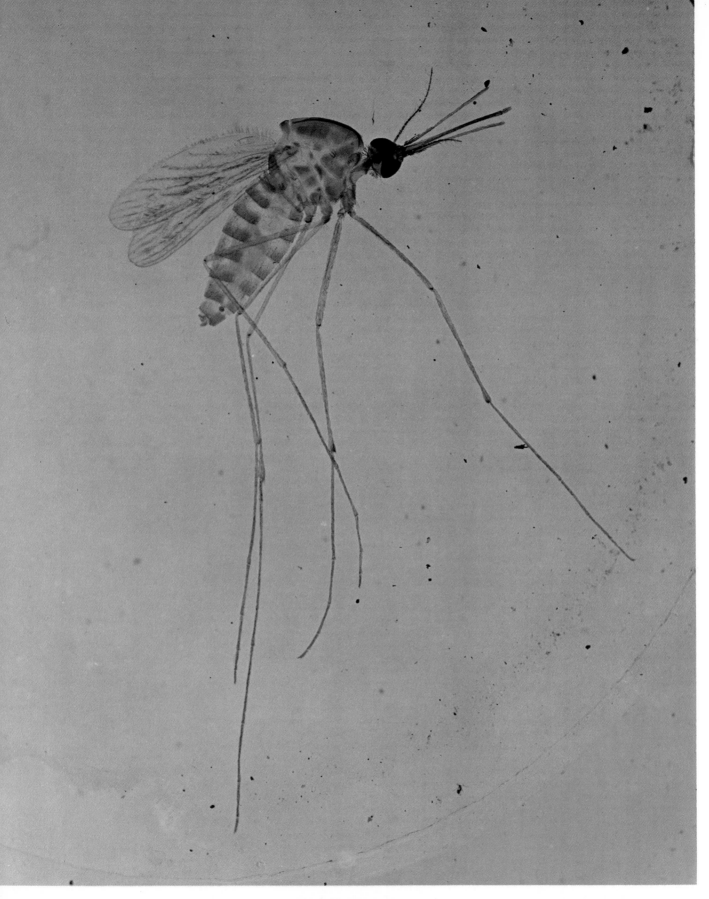

A VECTOR OF MALARIA

The mosquito *Anopheles quadrimaculatus*, responsible for most of the handful of U.S. malaria cases, is one of about 300 species that may carry various forms of the disease. Within the insect, malarial parasites picked up from human or animal hosts mature and reproduce, then mass in the salivary glands, whence they emerge when the insect takes another meal.

Malaria: From Mosquito to Man

Man is the reservoir and the *Anopheles* mosquito the carrier of the four species of protozoa that cause human malaria. Both play essential roles in the parasite's life cycle. Having reproduced sexually in the mosquito, the protozoon undergoes various phases of multiplication within the human host—first in the liver, then in red blood cells. These are burst apart as the parasite proliferates; the rhythmic outbreaks of protozoa in the blood cause the periodic high fever characteristic of the disease.

Collectively, the many species of malaria protozoa are probably the most widespread parasites in the world, affecting not only humans but also monkeys, rodents, birds and even some reptiles. Some experts believe that the parasites can infest such a variety of animals because they have evolved along with their hosts for millions of years. Human malaria afflicts tens of millions of people, though it is receding in the face of modern drugs and insecticides.

Monkeys, such as the rhesus shown above, suffer from a form of malaria akin to man's.

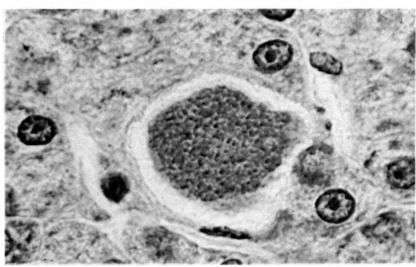

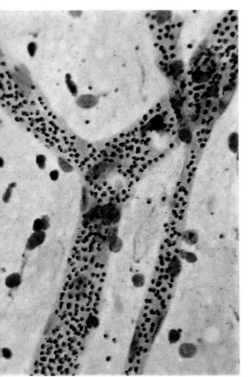

MALARIA FROM MONKEY TO MAN?
Monkey liver tissue shows signs of invasion by the malarial parasite *Plasmodium cynomolgi (above, center)*. As in man, the parasite lodges first in the liver, then attacks red blood cells. Recent experiments have proved that man can be infected with monkey malaria transmitted by mosquitoes, but it is not yet known if monkeys provide a natural reservoir for the disease.

ROADBLOCKS IN THE HUMAN BRAIN
Dark clusters of red blood cells infested with the parasite *Plasmodium falciparum* partially block the branching system of capillary vessels in a section of human brain tissue. Untreated, such clusters of affected cells may eventually shut off oxygen supply from the brain and cause death.

RESERVOIRS OF DANGER

Domestic livestock, like these long-horned Ankole cattle drinking at a Uganda water hole, are a prized but perilous possession in wide areas of Africa, where they serve as a natural reservoir for the microorganisms that cause sleeping sickness in man. Cattle are unaffected by the parasites that attack humans, but often suffer from an animal form of the disease.

AN UNAFFECTED HOST

Wild animals, like this roan antelope, have successfully adapted to the sleeping-sickness parasites that afflict and often kill both domestic animals and man. Domestication of antelopes has been proposed as a way of stepping up meat production in tsetse fly-infested areas.

Sleeping Sickness: Beast to Man

African trypanosomiasis, or sleeping sickness, is endemic among men and domestic animals in half of the African continent—the warm, wooded regions inhabited by the shade-loving tsetse fly, which serves as the disease vector. Sleeping sickness kills hundreds of people each year and seriously incapacitates thousands more. The disease begins with chills, fever and vomiting, and the victim develops enlarged lymph glands. Later, the parasite attacks the central nervous system, producing sleepiness and eventual death. Other forms of the disease exact a heavy toll among animals.

Like malaria, trypanosomiasis can be passed from man to man by its insect vector, but unlike malaria it is chiefly transmitted from animals—domestic and wild—to man. Microbiologists speculate that the parasite originally infested only animals. Later, it evolved two strains that attack humans. One, carried by a species of tsetse that feeds regularly on human blood, produces a mild form of the disease, because parasite and host have adapted to each other. The other, whose vector feeds chiefly on animal blood, produces severe sleeping sickness when the fly bites a human.

THE CAUSE OF THE DISEASE

The long-tailed parasite *Trypanosoma gambiense,* shown *(right)* among blood cells, is one of the two species of trypanosoma that cause human sleeping sickness. The various species look so much alike that they can be distinguished only by the effect they have on man and animals.

CLOSE-UP OF A CARRIER

Glossina palpalis, an African relative of the common house fly, is one of the 22 different species of tsetse fly that transmit trypanosomiasis to both humans and animals. Within the fly's body, the parasites multiply, then accumulate in the salivary glands in an infective form.

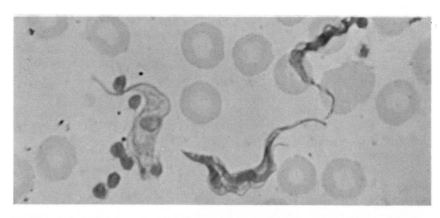

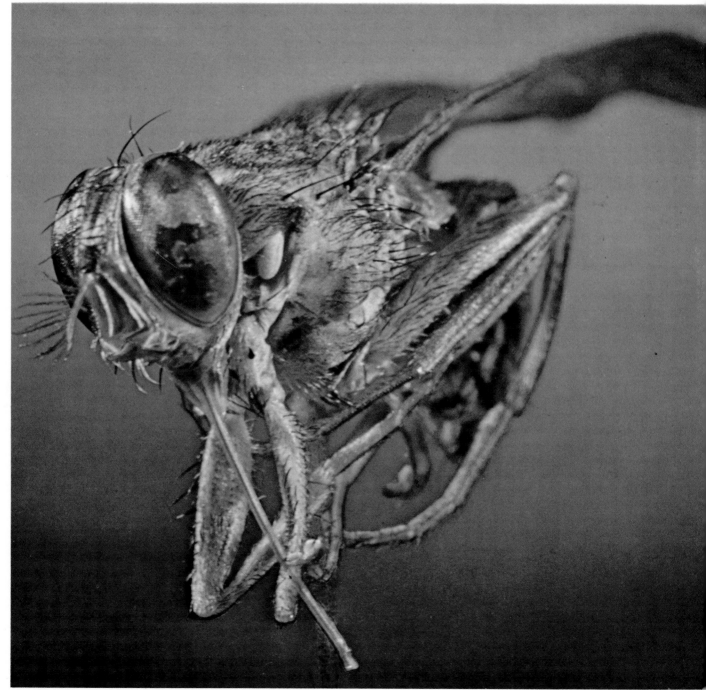

The Relay Route of Chagas' Disease

Chagas' disease—named after the Brazilian physician Carlos Chagas, who identified the single-celled creature, or trypanosome, that causes it —is a serious parasitic affliction to which 35 million people throughout Latin America are constantly exposed. About seven million become infected, and more than 10 per cent die. Both vertebrate animals and bugs are needed for the development of the Chagas parasite, which is relayed by the kissing bug *(below)* along an involved animal route that often leads to man.

As far as is known, animals that carry the trypanosome are not affected by it. But in man, the parasite causes fever, enlargement of the liver and spleen, and widespread tissue damage. Lodging in all kinds of tissue, the parasite's chief target is the heart. In advanced stages of the disease, the heart may be riddled with holes. Like many another disease, it most often afflicts those who can least afford to treat it: the rural poor.

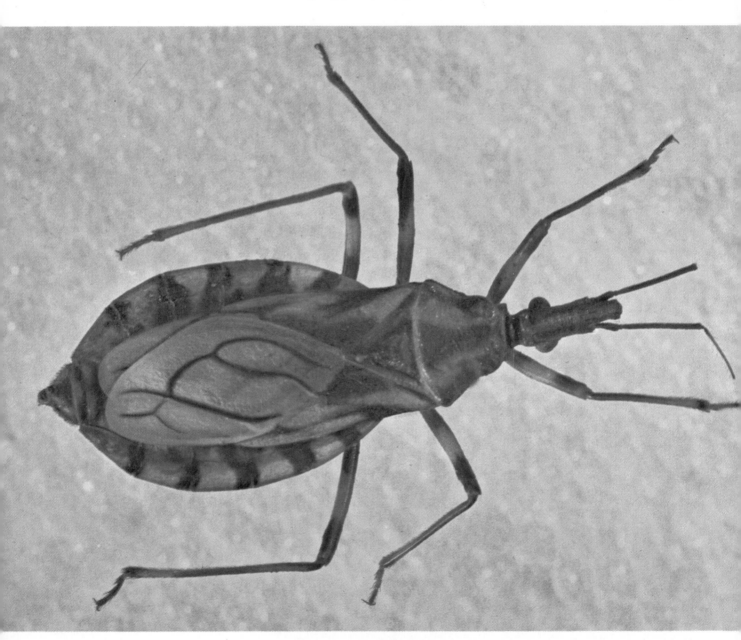

A BUG WITH A DISEASED KISS

"Kissing bugs"—a species that includes the *Triatoma braziliensis* of Brazil *(above)*—carry the parasite of Chagas' disease, excreting it as they suck human blood. The disease organism spends part of its life multiplying in the bug, then completes its cycle in animals or man. The bugs' popular name comes from their habit of biting tender parts of the human face.

A RETIRING JUNGLE HOST

Bony scales protect the jungle-dwelling arma- trypanosome that causes Chagas' disease, the
dillo *(above)* from larger predators—but not armadillo does not suffer from its role as host
from the small kissing bug, which finds chinks to the parasite—nor does it pose much of a
in the armor. An important wild host for the threat to humans, since it avoids settled areas.

A BOLD AND ROVING HOST

The opossum *(above)*, a roving feeder that both
hunts in the jungle and steals food from native
huts, provides the necessary liaison between
wild animal hosts and human victims. A domestic strain of the kissing bug may feed from
an infected opossum, then on a dog or a person.

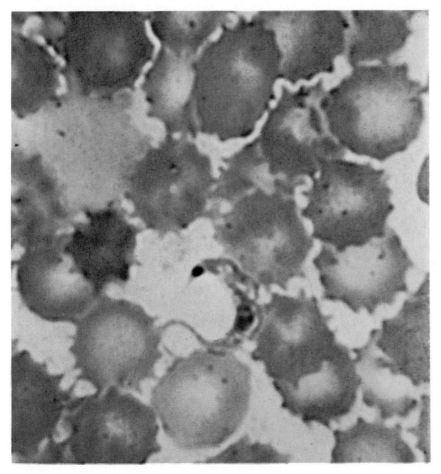

INSIDE THE HUMAN HOST

Trypanosoma cruzi, the Chagas parasite, coils
in a cluster of red blood cells in this photomicrograph *(left).* In affected persons the trypanosome multiplies first around the bite wound
and later in the heart. Pregnant women can
transmit the disease to their unborn children.

A DIGGER WITH A DISEASE

The Rocky Mountain wood tick shown in the picture above is the vector of Rocky Mountain spotted fever in the American West. The disease was first thought to be confined to the moun-tain region infested by this creature. But out-breaks of spotted fever in the East and else-where led to the discovery that rickettsiae can also be transmitted by a variety of other ticks.

A Fever of Ticks and Spots

In the last century, a number of early settlers in the American Northwest were stricken by a disease that an-nounced itself with a spotted rash, high fever and painful joints, then—for more than 20 per cent of the af-flicted—concluded in death. The dis-ease was named Rocky Mountain spotted fever, after the region where it first appeared.

Since then, cases of spotted fever have been found in many parts of the Western Hemisphere. The disease agent is a microorganism called *Rick-ettsia rickettsii (below)*. Smaller than a bacterium and larger than a virus, the organisms that cause spotted fe-ver normally live and multiply with-in ticks. The ticks, in turn, infest a series of animal hosts. As larvae and nymphs, ticks feed on the blood of rabbits and rodents such as ground squirrels *(opposite)*. As adults, they attach themselves to larger mammals, among them man. Though other large animals infested with the organism are unhurt by it, in man the rickett-siae damage the walls of small blood vessels; in advanced cases hemor-rhaging becomes widespread. Knowl-edge of how spotted fever is spread, plus modern treatment, have great-ly reduced the threat of the disease.

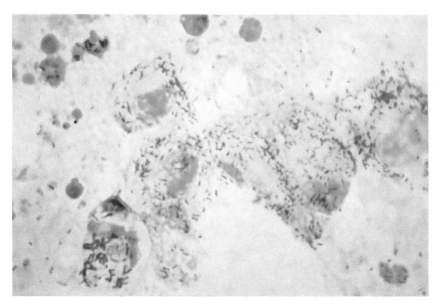

A PORTRAIT OF INFECTION

Red-stained rods of the spotted-fever microbes *Rickettsia rickettsii* infest bluish yolk-sac cells of a chicken embryo *(left)* in a laboratory photo-micrograph. In human tissue, the tiny micro-organisms multiply rapidly, damaging vessel walls and causing lesions throughout the body.

A RODENT RESERVOIR

A Columbian ground squirrel, a mountain rodent common to the northern United States and southern Canada, is a host to blood-gorged wood-tick nymphs clustered around its eyes and ears. No one animal species is known to be the basic reservoir for rickettsiae. Many small mammals carry them, and the tick vector itself passes the infection on through its eggs.

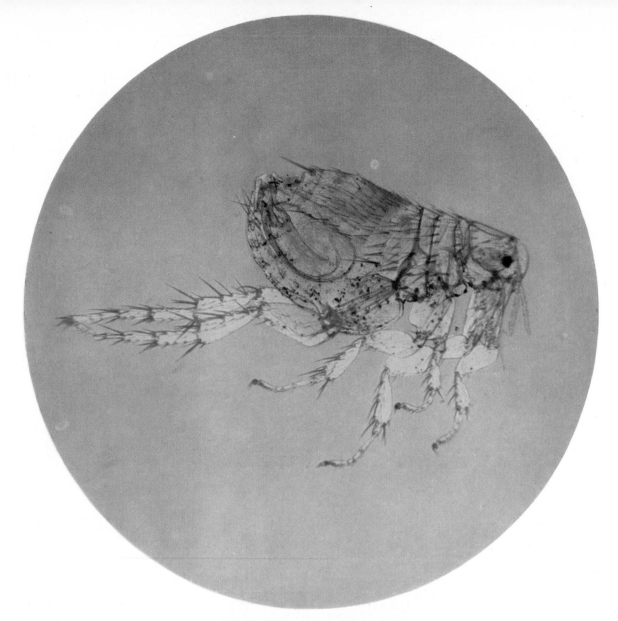

A Pestilence Spread by a Flea

Bubonic plague, once the most dreaded disease in the world, is transmitted by the bite of the common rat flea *(above)*. But the real villain in this disease is a bacillus, *Pasteurella pestis (right)*, which, once it is in the bloodstream, travels throughout the body, causing internal bleeding, delirium, headache, swollen lymph glands and excruciating boils in the groin, armpits and neck. The victim also runs a very high fever. Death occurs in from 25 to 50 per cent of untreated cases of bubonic plague. Though a minor threat in the U.S., bubonic plague occasionally flares up to create a serious menace in parts of Asia, Africa and South America.

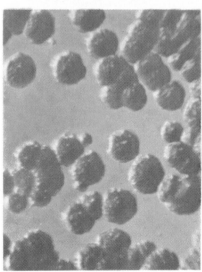

THE PARASITES OF PLAGUE
Deadly *Pasteurella pestis*, the bacillus that causes the plague, thrives in a laboratory culture medium *(above)*. The bacteria grow rapidly and group themselves into dome-shaped colonies.

A CARRIED CARRIER: THE FLEA
The rat flea, *Xenopsylla cheopis*, greatly magnified in the photomicrograph above, transmits the plague bacillus from animal to animal and from animal to man. Not itself a host for the disease, the flea spreads the infection by inoculating a new victim after feeding on a disease host.

THE FIRES OF PREVENTION
Scooped in by the shovelful, dead rats are burned in a Bombay furnace as a public-health measure. An urgent program to wipe out these bubonic-plague carriers was begun in 1952, when residents were urged to bring in rats for examination. Plague has dropped considerably since.

3
The Omnipresent Microbe

MICROCOSM dedicated to The London Water Companies. BROUGHT FORTH ALL MONSTROUS, ALL PRODIGIOUS THINGS, HYDRAS, AND GORGONS, AND CHIMERAS DIRE. *Vide Milton*

MONSTER SOUP commonly called THAMES WATER, being a correct representation of that precious stuff doled out

A CUP OF MONSTER SOUP
Long before anyone realized that microbes in drinking water could spread disease, many people in London were up in arms over the increasing pollution of the Thames River. This etching by the satiric artist William Heath appeared in the 1820s, some 30 years before the real danger of drinking "chimeras dire" was pointed out by the farsighted British physician John Snow.

THE SPREAD OF DISEASE has always seemed to man almost willfully erratic. Infectious illnesses attack some members of a population and leave others untouched. A disease that has taken a small, steady toll for generations may suddenly flare up as an epidemic. Strange and horrifying plagues have descended on whole nations apparently out of the blue.

Epidemiologists, who study the frequency and distribution of diseases, now know that man lives in a state of precarious equilibrium with the microorganisms that surround him. Most of the time, the relationship is surprisingly harmonious. Sooner or later, young, healthy humans come in contact with the bacteria and viruses native to their region, and develop a natural resistance to them by doing so. Illness occurs when, for some reason, this natural resistance no longer balances the virulence of the microbes. Sometimes individual resistance is insufficient, as when a child meets a germ for the first time; sometimes resistance is lowered by fatigue or ill health.

Occasionally, the balance of power between microbes and men is upset on a much wider scale. A foreign germ is imported to a region where it was unknown, a native one develops a mutant strain, or great numbers of people undergo some change unfavorable to their natural powers of resistance. The result may be an epidemic. Epidemics are not altogether erratic. They attend migrations, wars, social upheavals, undernourishment, squalor—any set of circumstances that gives microbes an edge.

The close connection between disease and an unfavorable environment was cruelly demonstrated to the Western world during the Industrial Revolution in the last century. Hundreds of thousands of people from rural areas migrated to the cities in search of new jobs, adventure and prosperity. What awaited them there, besides endless labor in unventilated factories, were living conditions so wretched that it became an achievement merely to survive.

Working-class families lived packed in dark and airless tenements, sometimes several families in one room. As many as 30 families might share one privy, connected to a cesspool which often overflowed into the street or cellar. Many households dispensed with the privies altogether, and simply emptied chamber pots out the nearest window. Some streets looked more like dunghills than thoroughfares. In New York City, it was reported, some houses could be reached only by wading through refuse that had accumulated to a depth of two or three feet. Slaughterhouses in the middle of the city (some next to elementary schools) added blood, dung and flies. The flies helped transmit a wide range of diseases.

Drinking water was sold by private companies, which simply piped it from the nearest source. In London, this was the Thames, in which raw sewage could be seen floating between reeking mudbanks. People drank the water unfiltered, complaining more about the chronic insufficiency of their local supply than about its dirtiness. The water companies did not bother to pipe water directly into working-class homes, but provided public taps from which water flowed for perhaps half an hour at a time, once a day or every other day. The poor stood in line for this water, bringing along whatever containers they had for storage—usually dirty ones without covers. This limited supply had to suffice for drinking and cooking; there was often little left over for washing.

The high cost of being poor

Diseases of all kinds flourished. In English cities, one out of every two children died before the age of five from tuberculosis, typhoid fever, dysentery, cholera or other pestilences. Such deaths were still regarded fatalistically in the early part of the century, and for a time cities did little to track down their causes. But as death rates rose, a few voices began to call for reform. In a report on the "Sanitary Conditions of the Labouring Population of Great Britain" in 1842, an English lawyer, Edwin Chadwick, showed that the poverty-stricken British laborers suffered a far higher incidence of disease than the middle and upper classes. Attributing this difference to the miserable conditions under which the workers lived, Chadwick declared that most of their diseases were preventable. His report laid the basis for the Great Sanitary Movement, a wave of reform that began in England and spread through the Western world.

The movement's goals were summed up in the program of one of the first voluntary citizens' groups to concern itself with public health, The Health of Towns Association. Formed in Britain soon after publication of the Chadwick report, the Association called for substituting "health for disease, cleanliness for filth, enlightened self-interest for ignorant selfishness," and demanded that everyone be given "the simple blessings of Air, Water and Light."

At first these demands met with violent opposition from slum landlords and water companies, who would be expected to pay for sanitary improvements. But a cholera epidemic in London in 1849 terrified even the well-to-do, and a large body of public opinion began to form in favor of the sanitarians. The 1849 epidemic was followed by another in 1853. This time a physician, John Snow, noted that most of the cholera victims were users of a busy public water pump in Broad Street. When asked how the epidemic might be stopped, Snow gave a reply that became a classic: "Remove the pump handle." Upon investigation, it was found that the well supplying the Broad Street pump was contaminated by a cesspool from a tenement in which a cholera patient lived.

Snow published a report in 1855 which clearly linked the cholera outbreak to contaminated water, but its implications were generally ignored. By tracing disease to a specific source, whence it had spread by contagion, Snow had jumped one step ahead of the medical knowledge of his time. For the early sanitarians, the enemy was simply "filth," particularly decomposing organic matter. Cholera and other pestilences were believed to rise from the odorous gases, or "miasmas," that accompanied decay. Miasmas seemed to explain as satisfactorily as unproved theories of contagion why epidemics favored the dirtiest and most evil-smelling parts of town.

So the sanitarians, practical men, concentrated their efforts on removing filth. To a large extent their approach worked. By clearing away dirt because it fouled the atmosphere, they removed the breeding ground of microbes and thus reduced the spread of many diseases. In the second half of the century, epidemics of typhus, typhoid, dysentery and cholera dramatically decreased.

The success of the sanitarians, however, can hardly be separated from the simultaneous work of social reformers and the enormous public impact of such novelists as Charles Dickens. Reformers demanded not only the removal of filth, but also more humane working conditions, the reduction of the grueling 69-hour week that was customary for factory laborers, and the end of child labor. As their efforts began to bear fruit in the second half of the 19th Century, some of the most flagrant evils attending the new industrial age were corrected. The subsequent rise in the standard of living did much to reduce death rates.

A contentious eminent Victorian

Foremost among the reformers in the field of health was John Simon, appointed the City of London's first Medical Officer of Health in 1848. Simon has been called "the greatest of Victorian civil servants." He created England's public health service, which became a model for the U.S. and other nations. His vividly written annual reports on London's health problems influenced a generation of Englishmen to accept the proposition that environmental conditions affect the spread and severity of disease. From this proposition emerged the modern science of epidemiology, in which the English still excel.

When Simon first took office, however, he had to contend with the Englishman's highly developed sense of domestic privacy. The city's right to compel house owners to connect privies to sewers, for example, was hotly disputed. But Simon believed that society was obliged to interfere in matters affecting public health, and he succeeded in persuading other public officials and the courts to back him up. He personally visited sewers, inspected residential and industrial nuisances, and pushed through laws that gave the city needed authority over sanitation. He markedly improved the effectiveness and safety of the city's system of smallpox vaccinations. He set up a weekly reporting system among local

PROTESTING UNSANITARY CONDITIONS, an indignant 1865 report on New York City included this print showing a slaughterhouse next to a public school. In these slaughterhouses, the accompanying text said, "large collections of offal are allowed to accumulate . . . constantly undergoing decomposition." The report, which also complained about fearful overcrowding and neglected sewers, led to the formation of the Metropolitan Board of Health in 1866.

55

health officers and registrars, to keep his department informed of trends in diseases and deaths. He crusaded for more abundant and purer water.

But urban epidemics could not be brought under really effective control until the mechanism of contagion was finally understood. Simon's experience with cholera gradually convinced him that ubiquitous miasmas were an insufficient explanation of disease. His conversion to the belief that every disease has a specific cause, and finally to the theory that germs cause disease, reflected the gradual changes in the scientific thinking of his time.

By the 1860s it had become clear that disease does not simply arise out of the air, but is spread by food, water and even people's hands. A Hungarian obstetrician, Ignaz Semmelweis, had already dramatically reduced the incidence of puerperal, or childbed, fever in a Vienna maternity ward by the simple expedient of requiring attending physicians to wash their hands in chlorinated water. A decade after John Snow's study of the Broad Street pump, health officials like Simon had come around to the view that it was dangerous to drink "fecalized water." At the same time, microbes—living organisms so tiny that they can be seen only under microscopes, if at all—were coming under intensive examination by scientists, among them a French chemist, Louis Pasteur. The final identification of microbes as the causes of infectious disease was the crowning achievement of 19th Century medical science.

The relatively large microbes known as bacteria had earlier been seen and described in detail by a 17th Century Dutch dry-goods dealer, Anton van Leeuwenhoek, who ground lenses as a hobby. His hobby became a passion, and his descriptions of the microscopic world he saw through his tiny, perfect lenses attracted so much attention that he was made a Fellow of England's Royal Society, one of the earliest and most distinguished scientific bodies of Europe.

Tiny creatures "prettily a-moving"

Over a period of 50 years, Leeuwenhoek wrote the Society hundreds of long, colloquial letters in which he described in precise detail the marvels he saw through his microscopes. In 1683 he wrote a particularly excited letter describing what he had found when he examined a drop of rainwater in which he had mixed some material taken from between his teeth. "I then saw, with great wonder, that in the said matter there were many very little living animalcules, very prettily a-moving," he wrote. Some "shot through the water like a pike," others "spun round like a top," and a third sort "went ahead so nimbly, and hovered so together, that you might imagine them to be a big swarm of gnats or flies." On another occasion, he looked at some material from his front teeth just after consuming large draughts of very hot coffee. To his astonishment he

AN EARLY MICROSCOPIST, Anton van Leeuwenhoek was honored by this Dutch stamp. The compound microscope had been invented by about 1590; however, Leeuwenhoek got better results than his contemporaries with his own specially ground single-lens magnifier. Besides drawing pictures of bacteria found in his mouth *(below)*, he also described the life cycle of the flea, and saw the movement of embryos in the eggs of a mussel.

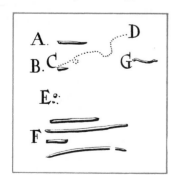

found the still corpses of bacteria under his lens. Trying again, this time with matter from his back teeth, he found animalcules moving as prettily as ever. He shrewdly deduced that the heat of the coffee had killed the little creatures that lay in its path.

Leeuwenhoek jealously guarded his secret method of grinding powerful lenses, with the result that when he died further investigation of the microcosm was slowed for lack of adequate instruments. Lenses had to be perfected anew by others, and it was not until the 19th Century that scientists were able to look clearly again at the minute creatures that swarmed about them.

Microbes seemed so mysterious that the chief scientific question in the first half of the 19th Century was not what they did, but where they came from. Some scientists were willing to concede that microbes probably generated their own kind, like other forms of life, but others held that they were spontaneously generated by putrefying substances.

Bacteria versus beet juice

Pasteur was the first to advance specific theories as to their powers. As a young chemist of 33, he was asked by a manufacturer of beet-juice alcohol to find out why vats of beet juice sometimes soured. Pasteur blamed bacteria. He also established to his own satisfaction that yeast, the classic fermenting agent used in the making of alcohol, was not a chemical, as was widely supposed, but a microbe. In 1857 he published a paper in which he declared that microbes caused milk to sour and wine to ferment. The paper went on to suggest that if microbes could cause fermentation, they might also cause disease.

Pasteur's explanation of fermentation was met with skepticism and even hostility, but his interest in microbes was unabated, and he pursued their study with further experiments. Seeking to solve the riddle of their origin, he discovered, by filtering air through cotton wool, that the air itself was filled with microbes. He next kept sterilized broth in glass flasks that sealed it against all but sterilized air. The broth generated no microbes. The genesis of microbes was not spontaneous after all; their presence could be controlled like that of any other organism.

In 1865 news of Pasteur's findings reached a British surgeon, Joseph Lister. Lister had long been appalled at the high death toll of surgical cases. Throughout Great Britain, roughly one out of every two amputations ended in the dreaded "hospital gangrene" or other infections, and in death. The toll seemed particularly tragic after the introduction of anesthetics widened surgical opportunities. Wishing to put to clinical test Pasteur's suspicion that microbes might cause diseases, Lister set out to destroy all germs that might land in his patients' wounds. After trying several disinfectants he hit upon carbolic acid, pouring it over wounds and spraying it around the operating field. Little attention had been paid to his predecessor, Ignaz Semmelweis, but Lister's timing was better: when his death rates fell, his colleagues were impressed. Almost single-handedly, Lister introduced antiseptic surgery to the world.

Tracking down diseases

Proof that germs cause disease accumulated. In 1876, Robert Koch, a German country doctor, demonstrated that anthrax—a disease common among cattle in his district and occasionally acquired by farmers—was caused by bacteria. A decade later Pasteur became convinced that another disease, rabies, was caused by microorganisms, even though they were so small that they remained invisible under the most powerful microscope available to him. He devised a way of growing the microbes in living animals, becoming the first to recognize and cultivate what later came to be called viruses.

Pasteur was also the first to divine that the principle of vaccination might apply to other diseases besides smallpox. He made the discovery by the kind of accident that, as he said, "favors only the prepared mind." Some chickens in his laboratory were inoculated with cultures of chicken cholera which had remained unused over a summer. The chickens failed to develop the disease. A fresh, highly virulent culture of the same bacillus was then prepared, and inoculated into the same chickens. To everyone's surprise, the chickens still did not die. Pasteur is said to have pondered this remarkable fact for a moment, then exclaimed, "Don't you see that these animals have been vaccinated!" Evidently all kinds of bacteria or viruses could be rendered harmless—either in the laboratory or, as in the case of smallpox, during passage through another species— and yet remain potent enough to immunize animals inoculated with them. Vaccination against many infectious diseases might become a general technique. Within four years, Pasteur had developed vaccines against chicken cholera, anthrax, swine erysipelas and—a most sensational event—rabies, a particularly dreadful killer.

Koch made still another discovery that shook the world in this golden age of microbiology. In 1882, applying the same tenacity he had used earlier in tracking down the anthrax bacterium, he succeeded in isolating the bacillus of tuberculosis—a disease most medical men believed was not contagious. Soon afterward, he developed a simple skin test, the tuberculin test, that made possible the detection of past or present infection.

Koch's success in isolating and cultivating the tubercle bacillus came at a time when the disease was the greatest single killer of the human race. Tuberculosis had been associated with cities since classical times. All during the 19th Century it had spread remorselessly with the growth

NATURAL IMMUNIZATION is the process by which the body's disease-fighting agents are produced by an actual attack of a disease. A virus enters certain body cells; using them as hosts, the virus multiplies and attacks other cells. In the process it stimulates cells called plasmacytes to produce antibodies; these turn on the virus and help in its destruction.

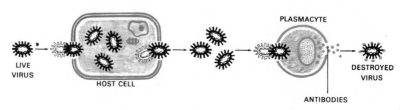

LIVE VIRUS

HOST CELL

PLASMACYTE

DESTROYED VIRUS

ANTIBODIES

of cities, until it had reached epidemic proportions throughout the industrialized world. It was known as the Great White Plague.

Its record in the U.S. was one of frightful devastation. Immigrants from Europe, many of them debilitated from famines at home, flooded into the poorest and dirtiest sections of cities, there to die of the disease by the thousands. Working children were infected in staggering numbers. Hundreds of thousands of children worked 12 hours a day, six days a week. Chronically exhausted and undernourished, they made particularly susceptible victims.

By 1857 the death rates in American cities from all causes were the highest in the Western world. New York had the worst rate, followed by Philadelphia and Boston, all with large immigrant populations. Much of the death toll was accounted for by tuberculosis, and the disease advanced across the nation as the frontier receded. Since tuberculosis was not considered contagious, its victims spread germs among those about them as they coughed, spat, and drank from family cups.

With improved sanitation, rising standards of living and, finally, Koch's proof that the disease was contagious, the death rates from tuberculosis began to decline without benefit of any cure through drugs. From a high point of about 400 deaths per 100,000 in the middle of the 19th Century, the mortality rate from tuberculosis fell in Europe and America to less than 200 per 100,000 by 1900. By 1945, the rate had dropped to less than 50 per 100,000. The natural resistance of the population was once again bringing the disease under control.

A persistent evil

By 1952, three drugs had been found to be effective in treating tuberculosis. The day of modern drugs was at hand, and many people jumped to the conclusion that the disease would shortly be eradicated. Yet tuberculosis is still with us today. The cycle of events that precipitated the Great White Plague in Western nations is now being repeated in the developing nations. Tuberculosis kills some three million persons each year in Asia, South America and Africa as these areas enter the cruel first stages of industrialization. Despite valiant efforts, the World Health Organization cannot yet control it. The cheapest of the drugs used to combat it, isoniazid, costs little more than salt, but for greatest effectiveness it must be given together with other drugs—and the administration of these drugs requires medical facilities that do not exist in most underdeveloped areas.

Elsewhere, the bacillus is merely quiescent. As recently as 1963, U.S. health officials concluded on the basis of tuberculin tests that some 35 million Americans have been infected with the tubercle bacillus at some time. Most have sufficient resistance to keep the infection at a standstill.

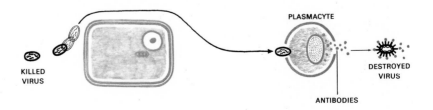

ARTIFICIAL IMMUNIZATION through vaccination prevents disease while preventing damage to host cells. In this case the virus, killed in the laboratory, is unable to enter host cells to multiply. However, the virus retains the ability to stimulate plasmacytes to produce antibodies, which then ward off future attacks of live virus *(far right)*.

KILLED VIRUS

PLASMACYTE

DESTROYED VIRUS

ANTIBODIES

But any catastrophic change in American living standards would once more make tuberculosis a threat to millions of people across the nation.

Not surprisingly, the disease has a way of flaring up in pockets of poverty. Although U.S. mortality from TB had fallen to 4.9 per 100,000 by 1963, the rate of new cases had started to rise again in big cities. Few American children have had the opportunity to acquire immunity. In 1964, worried by a sudden increase in active cases of tuberculosis in Harlem and other slum areas, New York City started to vaccinate school-children on a mass scale.

The mixed blessing of progress

Although the microbes of tuberculosis and many other infectious diseases still survive, better sanitation has drastically reduced the number of occasions on which the members of civilized societies come in contact with them. Yet reduced exposure to disease has proved to be a strangely mixed blessing. Success in minimizing the spread of infections among children has transformed certain so-called "childhood diseases" into serious hazards for adults. Childhood diseases, as such, do not exist: no infection is peculiar to childhood. The term came to be applied to certain illnesses simply because, until recently, almost everybody got them early and acquired a lifelong immunity. Children between five and 15, furthermore, pass through what has been called the "golden age of resistance," a period in which their resistance to disease is far higher than that of infants and adults. Hence children in this age-group can endure common illnesses with light symptoms and little harm done. Mumps in a child, for example, sometimes hardly requires bed rest. But mumps in an adult can cause havoc throughout his entire system, make him miserable for weeks, and may even leave behind permanent glandular damage.

More and more of the familiar childhood diseases are now attacking adult victims. For example, many children now grow up without being exposed to German measles, with the result that the disease still hangs over them as adults. This is particularly dangerous in the case of pregnant women, for the German-measles virus can severely damage a fetus during its first three or four months of development. Possible damage includes deafness, blindness, retardation and congenital malformations of the heart.

Poliomyelitis, too, found victims in a new age-group and became more damaging as it became less frequent. Polio infections were once common among babies everywhere, although they were generally so mild that they went unrecognized. Infants often contracted the infection while they still carried maternal antibodies to help them fight it off. In primitive countries even today, most children have had mild cases and have developed antibodies to all three types of polio by the time they are

AN UNDERGROUND ORDEAL awaits a boy and girl being lowered into a British coal mine. Until 1842, when Parliament barred all women and boys under 10 from the pits, one third of Britain's miners were under 18, some as young as four. Working under miserable conditions, youngsters grew up stunted, and suffered asthma and tuberculosis.

two. Since the virus often spreads through contaminated water, it is particularly prevalent in areas with poor sanitation.

With the general rise in living standards in the West, however, most of the sources of polio infection disappeared, and with them the chance for the population to build up early immunity. Around the 1920s, the paralytic form of the disease became more frequent, turning up first in the U.S. and Sweden—two countries with high standards of sanitation. It could no longer be called a children's disease. Its chief victims were young adults, and it caused far more devastation among them than it had among children. It paralyzed not only arms and legs but respiratory systems and whole bodies. Only the development of polio vaccines in the 1950s brought the crippling disease under control.

A baffling foe

In short, man's modern skill in the prevention and control of disease has succeeded to some extent in stripping civilized populations of their natural immunities, leaving them acutely vulnerable when virulent germs do attack. It is difficult to foresee a solution to this unprecedented problem. No amount of technological wizardry is likely to succeed in wiping out the microbes that can cause disease. They are too prolific, too adaptable and too widespread to be made to disappear from the face of the earth.

Nor can vaccines supply the whole answer. So many kinds of bacteria and viruses exist that at present it is impossible to vaccinate people against all of them. The great success of the smallpox vaccine comes from the fact that until now only one strain of smallpox virus has been known. The pneumococcus and streptococcus bacteria, on the other hand, together have at least 100 different strains; a vaccine against only one of them would be next to useless.

To complicate matters further, some germs have an alarming way of developing new strains that are unaffected by existing vaccines and drugs. The greatest pandemic of modern times, the influenza outbreak of 1918-1919, probably resulted from a mutant strain of influenza virus. The mortality it caused was appallingly high: between 10 and 20 million persons died throughout the world. Most of the deaths were attributable to the pneumonia which arose from secondary bacterial infections when the flu victims' resistance was low. Had today's antibiotic drugs been available, many lives probably could have been saved. But even today some pneumonias cannot be cured by drugs because the microbes have developed antibiotic-resistant strains. Almost none of the virus-caused diseases can be treated successfully with drugs. It is not inconceivable that a new microbial strain could cause a worldwide pandemic at any time, against which all the drugs of modern medicine would be futile.

"AH! YOU MAY LAUGH, MY BOY; BUT IT'S NO JOKE BEING FUNNY WITH THE INFLUENZA!"

MAKING FUN OF FLU, a 19th Century cartoon reflects the attitude of many people that it is hard to take too seriously an affliction whose characteristic symptoms are red eyes and a runny nose. But influenza was well known as a killer even before its dramatic pandemic of 1918 and 1919. This *Punch* drawing was a wry comment on a severe epidemic which ravaged England in 1847, claiming at least 5,000 lives and attacking one quarter of London's 2.1-million population.

Changes in social patterns can also alter or revive a disease. The incidence of gonorrhea and syphilis—diseases supposedly conquered by penicillin in the early 1950s—has risen sharply in recent years, returning to its post-World War II level and even exceeding it in some places. It has been estimated that one U.S. teenager is infected with venereal disease every 11 minutes. Part of the rise can be attributed to a relaxation of public programs against VD and a false sense of security based on drugs. While gonorrhea is one of the easiest diseases to cure in its early stages, requiring only a few shots of penicillin, its microbes persist, especially in women. Such lingering infections are difficult, and sometimes impossible, to detect. Eliminating the sources of venereal infection has proved far more difficult than curing venereal disease—with the result that, in spite of drugs, the disease continues to spread.

Useful as modern drugs may be in treating or curing disease, they are now undergoing a critical reappraisal as it becomes clear that microbes have powers that remain beyond the magic of medicine. Sanitation, rising living standards and vaccinations, without the aid of drugs, have brought the major epidemics under control in most of the industrialized nations. Thanks to drugs, of course, man's burden of illness is greatly eased. But despite recent optimism, microbial diseases are a constant threat—and they will remain so as long as microbes exist.

The Battle against Infection

Until the 19th Century, so little was known about the contagious diseases which often scourged whole populations that only the black magic of superstition could be invoked to explain them. Influenza got its name because it was blamed on celestial influence, malaria because it was thought to be caused by bad air. But a few observers detected a correlation between filth and disease, and there were some isolated efforts at sanitation. Beginning in 1860, a triumvirate of scientific masterminds—Louis Pasteur (*opposite*), Joseph Lister and Robert Koch —subjected contagion to a withering attack. Alternately borrowing ideas from one another and contributing theories of their own, these men proved that germs could cause contagious disease, and that the germs causing specific diseases could be isolated and identified. Finally a weapon was developed to immunize against many infectious diseases that had devastated mankind for centuries.

GENIUS OF THE LABORATORY
Poring over a laboratory flask, Louis Pasteur, the French chemist, examines the rabies-infected spinal cord of a rabbit. Although he is popularly remembered for the germ-killing process called pasteurization, Pasteur pioneered in the isolation of bacteria, and developed the first man-made immunizing agents against such diseases as anthrax, chicken cholera and rabies.

Fighting Filth in the Hospitals

Hospitals of the early 1800s rarely had running water, and what water they had was usually contaminated. Garbage, human wastes and assorted offal were dumped into a pit in the courtyard. Surgeons wiped their instruments on their trousers; bedclothes were rarely changed. Hospital infection was rampant—up to one third of all women giving birth died of puerperal fever, a form of blood poisoning. As late as mid-century only a few visionaries recognized any connection between filth and disease. Among them was philosopher Oliver Wendell Holmes *(opposite)*, himself a trained physician, who wrote an indignant paper on the contagiousness of puerperal fever in 1843.

An even greater concern gripped a Hungarian-born obstetrician, Ignaz Semmelweis, after he took a post at a Vienna hospital in 1846. He noted that in one ward, tended by students fresh from dissecting cadavers, one patient in eight died of puerperal fever. In another, ministered by midwives who were not thus contaminated, the death rate was much lower. Semmelweis ordered all attendants to wash their hands. A year later the death rate in his ward had dropped to zero. Despite this success, hospital authorities refused to be convinced, and in 1850 an anguished and frustrated Semmelweis returned to his native Budapest, where his ideas finally received limited acceptance.

SCENE OF A DOCTOR'S TRIUMPH
At Budapest's St. Rochus Hospital, Ignaz Semmelweis was made Professor of Obstetrics and given freedom to enforce his antiseptic practices in a ward assigned to him. Although the rest of the hospital remained typically dirty, and the incidence of hospital infection remained typically high, puerperal fever virtually disappeared among patients in Semmelweis' ward.

AN ENEMY—AND VICTIM—OF DIRT
Ignaz Philipp Semmelweis antagonized most of his fellow obstetricians by criticizing their unclean surgical practices. In an open letter to the profession he even called some of them "murderers." Ironically, he died of the blood poisoning he had fought so hard to prevent.

BIRTHPLACE OF A PROPHETIC PAPER
In this room in his Boston home, Dr. Oliver Wendell Holmes, the American physician, wit and philosopher, composed his attack on the medical practices that spread childbed fever. Holmes had earlier left private medical practice to write and to teach medicine at Harvard.

CONCLAVE ON INFECTION
O. W. Holmes sits second from left in a photograph of the Society for Medical Improvement, before which he presented his "Contagiousness of Puerperal Fever." Published in 1843, the paper was largely ignored until 1847, when he became Dean of Harvard Medical School.

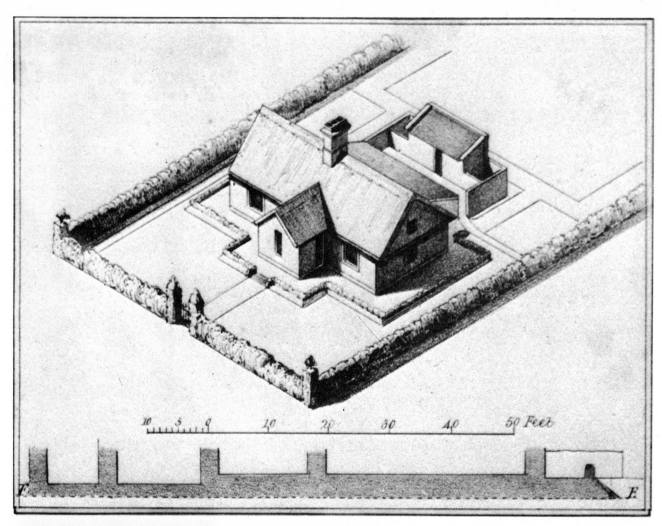

A BOLD PLAN FOR HOUSING
At a time when most workers lived in crowded tenements or squalid shacks, Edwin Chadwick's report recommended this laborer's cottage as public housing. It was to be elevated slightly for good drainage and so situated that at least one side would always be in the sunlight. Another innovation called for the outhouse and cesspool to be located far away from the well.

EARLY ADVOCATE OF SANITATION
Although Sir Edwin Chadwick's ideas rapidly took hold, his bluntness antagonized many important people. Because of this he was retired —with a large pension—when he was only 54.

Cleaning Up the Cities

Although hospitals of the 19th Century were slow to adopt antiseptic techniques, the 1840s saw some remarkable strides in sanitation outside the hospitals. One of the most noteworthy of these advances was pushed through by England's Sir Edwin Chadwick. A lawyer by profession, he had long been concerned about the living conditions of the poor. In 1832 he was commissioned by the British Government to make a formal study of these conditions.

Chadwick's report, issued in 1842, contained far-reaching recommendations. Among other things, it urged public construction of single-family houses to eliminate crowding, with each house on a plot large enough for a garden and lawn. With an eye to the psychological well-being of the working people, Chadwick proposed parks for the enjoyment of sunlight and air. But his most revolutionary recommendation was for an underground sewage system to remove the household wastes which had previously been consigned to the streets.

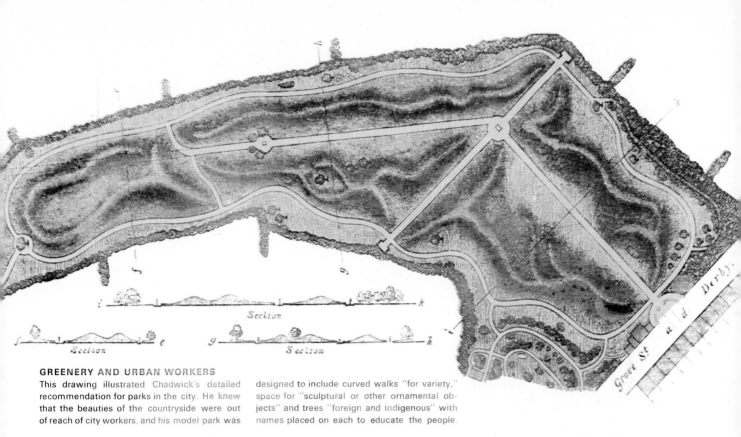

GREENERY AND URBAN WORKERS

This drawing illustrated Chadwick's detailed recommendation for parks in the city. He knew that the beauties of the countryside were out of reach of city workers, and his model park was designed to include curved walks "for variety," space for "sculptural or other ornamental objects" and trees "foreign and indigenous" with names placed on each to educate the people.

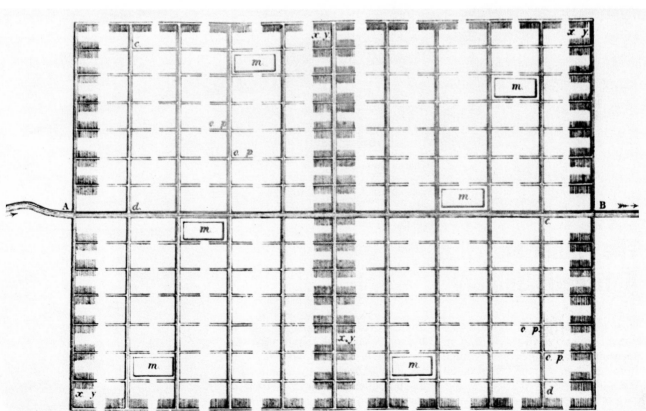

A MODEL SEWAGE SYSTEM

Before Sir Edwin Chadwick's time, sewers existed only in a few of the larger cities. His idea was to connect sewer lines to every house, to carry wastes far from homes and drinking-water supplies. He also was among the first to recognize the danger of having sewage empty into the rivers. His report noted that it was "a pity that so much valuable manure should be lost to the land, and be discharged into rivers to their contamination and obstruction." To eliminate this condition, he suggested that the wastes be piped to farmland for use as fertilizer.

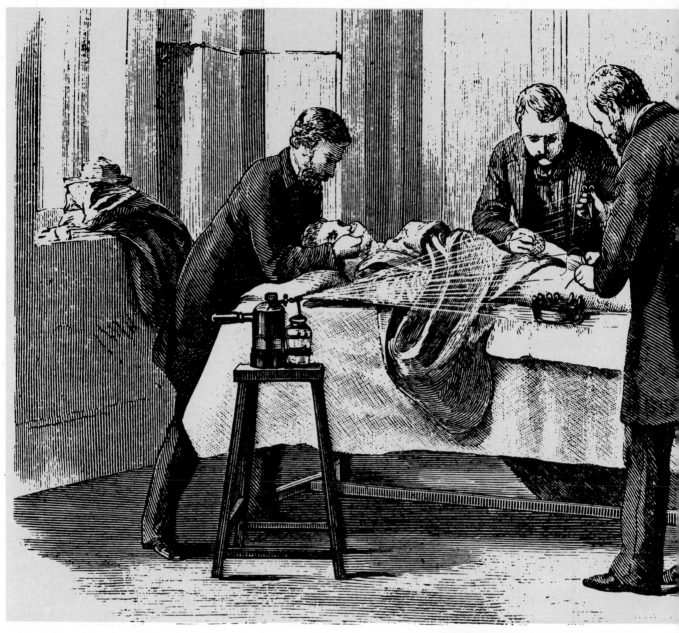

The Father of Antiseptic Surgery

During the first part of the 19th Century, about half of all people who underwent amputations died, usually from infection. In the 1860s, a 33-year-old University of Glasgow surgery professor named Joseph Lister noted that simple bone fractures—those in which the skin was unbroken—almost always healed without complication, while compound fractures were often followed by infection and death. Lister had read Pasteur's references to airborne microbes, and he became convinced that these were the cause of wound infection. He experimented with many chemicals to kill microbes and finally settled on carbolic acid. Not only did he apply the solution to wounds and instruments; he even sprayed the air around the operating table *(above)* in his campaign to destroy bacteria that produce infection. He was knighted for the brilliant success he achieved.

Baron Lord Lister (1827-1912)

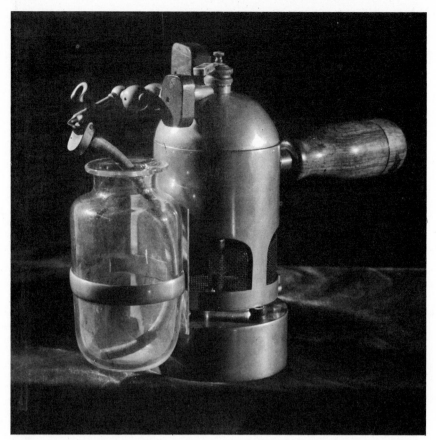

A MEDICAL PIONEER'S TOOL

Above is the carbolic-acid sprayer actually used by Lister in many operations. The glass bottle holds a solution of one part carbolic acid to 100 parts of water. Steam, which was generated in the metal container, atomized the solution, forcing it over the operating table in a fine spray. Lister later realized that sterilization of the wound was sufficient and discarded the sprayer.

SPRAYING FOR SAFETY

In this 1882 engraving surgeons perform an operation beneath the carbolic mist of a Lister sprayer. Americans and Germans adopted Lister's methods almost immediately, but it was 15 years before his own countrymen recognized his contribution and accepted his techniques.

LIGATURES BY LISTER

One of Lister's contributions to surgery was his strong, antiseptic ligatures that held blood vessels until they healed, then were absorbed by the tissue without causing infection. The jar at right contains catgut ligatures made by Lister in the 1860s and kept antiseptic in carbolic acid.

Dramatic Results from the Laboratory

Louis Pasteur was a tireless medical mastermind who drove himself and his staff pitilessly. Yet at heart he was a squeamish sentimentalist. In 1885, having developed and tested his rabies vaccine successfully and repeatedly on animals, Pasteur was faced with an agonizing decision. On July 6 of that year, a young Alsatian named Joseph Meister was brought to Pasteur. Two days before, the youngster had been bitten a number of times on his hands and legs by a rabid dog. Physicians told Pasteur that certain death awaited the boy within a month.

The vaccine had never been tried on a human, and Pasteur could not bring himself to make a decision immediately. But the next day, still beset by doubts, Pasteur gave his permission—though he refused to give the first injection himself. The inoculations were given by a physician (*opposite*). The boy was the first of thousands the vaccine saved from death.

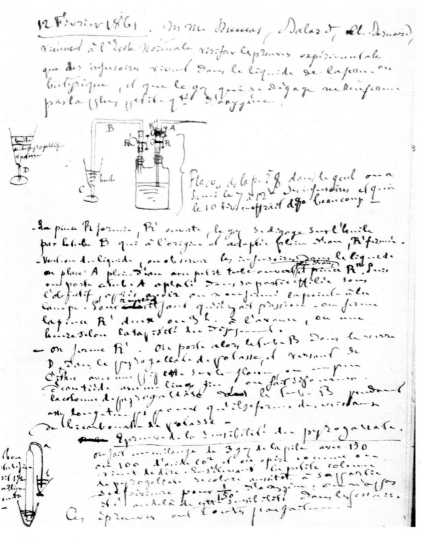

SOME NOTES ON RANCID BUTTER

The page above, taken from Pasteur's notebook, describes an experiment in which he sought to establish the conditions under which different varieties of bacteria live. He sealed in a flask the bacteria that produce butyric acid—which is found in rancid butter—and demonstrated that unlike many bacteria, they can exist only in an environment in which oxygen *is not* present.

A DEVOTED CARETAKER
Joseph Meister was so grateful to Pasteur for saving him from rabies that he became caretaker of the Pasteur Institute in Paris, where this photograph was taken in the 1930s. He committed suicide in 1940 rather than unlock Pasteur's crypt to invading Nazi soldiers.

RESCUED FROM RABIES
As Pasteur anxiously watches, young Joseph Meister, bitten by a mad dog in 1885, becomes the first human being to receive Pasteur's anti-rabies treatment. Prior to Pasteur no one could be sure he would survive the bite of a mad dog.

71

Dead Aim on Deadly Diseases

A PORTRAIT OF ANTHRAX
This drawing, excerpted from Koch's original paper explaining how the anthrax bacillus could be cultivated, shows the bacteria in various stages of growth with their beadlike spores.

Infectious disease in the human body is roughly analogous to an infestation of insects in a garden. It is easier to cure if the type of bug causing the damage can be identified. The all-important technique for isolating and identifying the microbe responsible for a disease was perfected by a German country doctor named Robert Koch. Koch succeeded in discovering the life cycle of the anthrax bacillus in 1876. His technique involved isolating the organism from other microbes, cultivating it in a pure culture, infecting an animal with this purified culture and finally isolating the microbe again from the infected animal.

After his initial discovery, Koch was sent by the Governments of Great Britain and Germany on expeditions to study diseases in remote parts of the world. In India and Africa, he looked into the nature of cattle plague and sought the cause of sleeping sickness. In addition, he helped establish that bubonic plague is transmitted by the fleas of the black rat. But his most celebrated discovery was that of the bacillus that causes tuberculosis.

A HOMEMADE LABORATORY
In his makeshift laboratory in Wollstein, Germany, shown reconstructed in this picture, Koch performed his historic research on anthrax. His only professional equipment was the microscope given him by his wife. He built the photographic equipment at left, used kitchen plates for laboratory dishes and potato slices as the nutrient surfaces on which to grow bacteria.

A STUDY OF SLEEPING SICKNESS
In a photograph taken in East Africa in 1906, Koch (facing the camera) and his aides are shown taking blood samples for diagnosing sleeping sickness. Word of the research spread through the area, and so many natives appeared a compound was built to accommodate them.

4
Diseases of Starvation and Surfeit

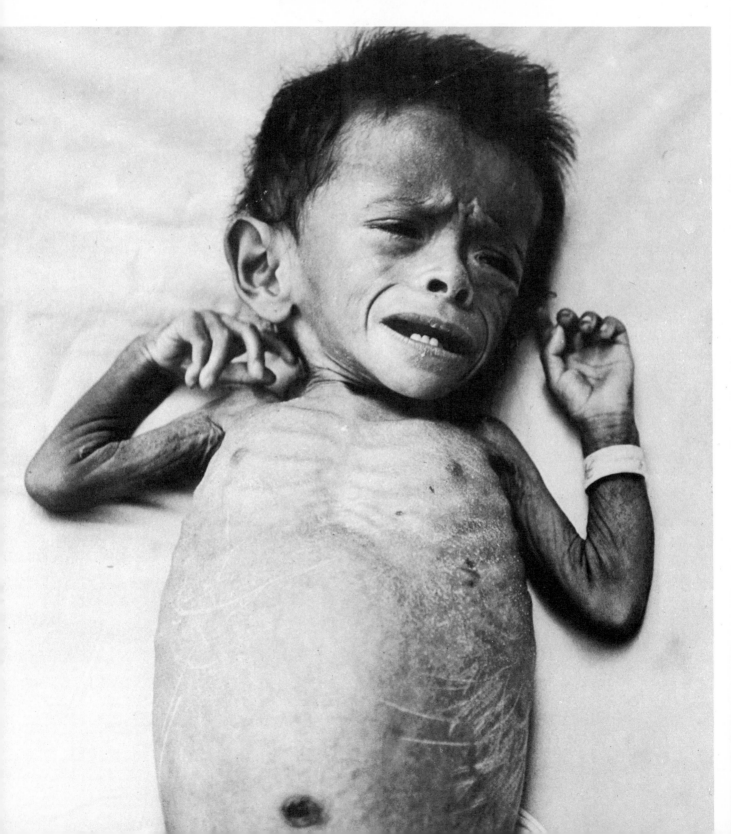

THE SCIENCE OF NUTRITION, which began to develop rapidly in the 19th Century, put an end to the view of food as simply food and focused instead on the various chemicals of which it is composed. One by one these chemical nutrients were isolated and related to health. Then, as scientists established the proper relationships between these chemicals, they discovered that a scanty but well-balanced diet is infinitely superior to a lavish but unbalanced one. Having defined the essential nutrients, scientists next learned how to manufacture a number of them, in the form of protein supplements, mineral additives, vitamin pills and so on.

These were all spectacular advances, but they left most of the world unaffected. Around the globe, malnutrition and the many diseases that follow in its wake still cripple or kill millions of men, women and children who might be healthy if they had a chance to benefit from modern knowledge. In Africa, Asia and Latin America live thousands of strangely swollen children, their bellies bloated, their cheeks blubbery, their skin splotchy, their hair discolored. They are victims of protein starvation. Much of their "fat" is really swelling caused by excess fluid in the body tissues. Their disease, which went generally unrecognized until the 1940s, is called kwashiorkor, from two words of the African Ga dialect meaning "first" and "second": i.e., the sickness that strikes the first child when he is displaced at his mother's breast by the secondborn.

Kwashiorkor often develops in these babies soon after they have been weaned. As long as they get enough mother's milk, they grow normally. But when their diet shifts to the thin, starchy gruels that are standard fare in underdeveloped nations, they may become dangerously ill. Such a child quickly loses his appetite and often develops diarrhea. These symptoms lead his mother to cut down his rations even further, thus aggravating the disease. The child's liver becomes grossly enlarged. His skin sometimes pales as its pigment becomes concentrated into curious black patches that peel off in shreds. Soon he sinks into a profound apathy, interrupted only by spells of irritability. If left untreated, the child often dies—either of acute protein starvation or from any one of the countless infections which, abounding in underdeveloped areas, flare up whenever the body's resistance is low.

Protein malnutrition, of which kwashiorkor is the extreme example, is the most widespread and serious nutritional disease in the world today. It seems particularly prevalent wherever people are struggling through the difficult transitional stages from completely primitive societies—where the diet, though strange by civilized standards, may be relatively well-balanced—to an industrialized way of life. To a large extent protein malnutrition is responsible for the staggering death rate among young children in pre-industrial societies—a rate between 10 and 60

SIGNS OF STARVATION
The swollen belly, roughened skin and lusterless hair of the one-year-old Guatemalan girl opposite are classic symptoms of advanced malnutrition. In this case, starvation has taken the form of a condition called marasmus (from the Greek word for "a wasting"), caused by a diet poor in quantity and quality, and sometimes by the body's inability to absorb food.

times that of the U.S. In a two-year study of four Guatemalan villages, it was found that of 222 deaths of one- to four-year-olds, most had been listed officially as due to worms. Yet researchers discovered that nearly 40 per cent of the victims had shown definite symptoms of kwashiorkor. The worms and most of the other afflictions that killed these children would not have been fatal to well-nourished children.

Just as significant as this high mortality are the insidious effects of chronic protein malnutrition upon the millions of children who survive but remain forever stunted, weakened and vulnerable to disease. As adults, they cannot do much useful work, a fact that helps perpetuate their regions' low standards of living.

A paradox of hunger

Protein hunger is an everyday, unchanging fact of life for great numbers of the world's people, many of whom are hard put to get any food at all. In parts of India and China, for example, the consumption of meat and dairy products—the natural foods containing the most complete proteins—is almost nil. In such regions animals cannot be raised for food, since they return only a fraction of the calories, or energy, they consume—an important consideration in countries where a poor rice crop can mean the death of millions and where a polite salutation between friends is, "Have you eaten?"

Famines and malnutrition, of course, have existed since the beginning of time. But today there is a cruel paradox: man has all the knowledge necessary to produce enough properly balanced food to feed the entire population of the world. It is now known that in addition to carbohydrates and fats, which provide energy, man needs at least 40 other nutrients, and that a deficiency of any one of them can cause illness. Vitamins, which monopolized the attention of nutritionists in the 1930s and 1940s, are now produced on a large scale. Minerals could be made available where needed. Even proteins, now in such desperately short supply around the world, could be made plentiful by science. It is all a question of priorities, and money.

The proteins, currently the most expensive of foods to obtain in high-quality form, are also among the most vital to human beings. They are large, complex chemical substances made up of varying combinations of some 20 amino acids. At least 10 are essential in the diet of man. They all promote growth during the crucial childhood years and aid in the renewal of tissues. In nature, proteins are first manufactured by plants, using nitrogen, oxygen, hydrogen and carbon from the soil and air. Thus both man and animals depend ultimately on plants for proteins. But most of the commonly eaten plant products contain incomplete proteins: they lack some of the essential amino acids, or have them in the wrong proportions. And the absence of even one essential amino acid limits the body's ability to make use of the others.

In the wealthy countries, animals are used as virtual factories for the production of high-quality proteins in concentrated form. But it is not necessary to eat meat, eggs or dairy products to stay healthy. The Japanese get a large percentage of their protein from soybeans and other vegetables. Some primitive tribes have learned to eat various leaves, berries, insects and even clays, all of which are rich in nutrients they would otherwise lack. But a dreadful monotony marks the diet of people in more and more nations as they specialize in agricultural products for world markets. Some parts of Latin America now produce almost nothing but coffee for export, while others grow mainly bananas or sugar cane. The Brazilian northeast provides a tragic example of a region where people are now starving because, under the single-crop system, they must concentrate all their efforts on producing sugar. In many Central American nations as well, governmental policies have encouraged the production of cash crops, particularly cotton, at the expense of food crops necessary to balanced diets.

The usual Central American diet of corn and beans, or just corn, is so deficient in certain essential amino acids that it accounts for much of the traditional lethargy of the people there. Many peasants who have been raised on this diet no longer feel genuine appetite; they content themselves with a few cornmeal *tortillas*, and sometimes must force themselves to eat even those. Besides suffering from a shortage of proteins, Central Americans also lack minerals and vitamins. When in addition they become infested with worms or other parasites, they have little energy left, even though they may not actually look sick. A serious infestation of hookworm can rob its victim of half a pint of blood per day, leading to fatal anemia.

Flour of health

To help restore proper diets, much scientific effort in recent years has gone into producing inexpensive foods with just the right balance of amino acids, for use in countries where animal proteins are unavailable to all except a wealthy minority. Many of these efforts have stressed local production of locally acceptable foods based on cheap, available crops. Probably the most ambitious project of this kind is that of the Institute of Nutrition of Central America and Panama (INCAP), the organization which conducted the survey of kwashiorkor in Guatemala. Seeking a new diet for Central American children, INCAP found a way in which the emphasis on cotton as a cash crop could actually be turned to advantage. The cotton industry yields large quantities of cheap cottonseed meal as a by-product. INCAP's nutritionists studied methods

THE FACES OF FAMINE are seen in these German children sketched by Käthe Kollwitz during the Depression after World War I, and in the cold statistical chart below. History's most terrible famines have resulted from crop failure due to drought, blight and insect plagues, but wars, floods and earthquakes have also taken their toll. Overpopulation, poor communications and single-crop economies make many nations particularly vulnerable.

MAJOR FAMINES SINCE 1650		
DATE	PLACE	DEATHS
1669-1670	BENGAL	3,000,000
1769-1770	BENGAL	10,000,000
1816-1817	IRELAND	737,000
1838	NORTHERN INDIA	800,000
1846-1847	IRELAND	1,000,000
1860-1901	INDIA (10 FAMINES)	15,000,000
1876-1879	NORTHERN CHINA	9,500,000
1921-1922	RUSSIA	3,000,000
1943	BENGAL	1,500,000

of purifying this meal into a flour for human consumption. At this time they tried out several formulas that would supplement the flour, ground-up local corn and other cheap foods to form a complete protein meal.

INCAP's ninth formula, perfected in 1959 after nearly 10 years of work, proved so effective that the Institute began large-scale efforts to manufacture and distribute it in Guatemala City and nearby towns and villages. Named Incaparina (*harina* is the Spanish word for flour), it consists of 38 per cent cottonseed flour, 58 per cent grain, and a number of added vitamins and minerals.

Proteins for preschool growth

It had been shown earlier that even when protein supplements were fed to Central American schoolchildren, their height and weight did not achieve the standard for their age. It seemed that they could never make up for the arrested development of their earliest years. But when INCAP tried giving protein supplements to *preschool* children, the results were dramatic: the children gained weight and grew rapidly.

Evidence soon began to accumulate that early protein supplements also greatly heightened resistance to disease. For three years, three rural Indian villages in Guatemala served as a testing ground for INCAP scientists. In one village they gave supplements to all children under five years of age. In another, they paid no attention to nutrition but made every effort to prevent infection by improving sanitation; whenever a young child did fall ill they gave him prompt treatment. The third village, in which nothing was done, served as a control. In the middle of the experiment an epidemic of measles broke out. Each village had 40 to 60 cases among the children under study. In the control village five children died of the disease; in the village where only medical treatment was provided, the rate was equally high. But among the children who received the extra protein, there was not a single fatality.

In its efforts to get Incaparina into wider use, INCAP was careful to observe local customs and taboos. In Guatemala milk and eggs are regarded as "man's food," "too heavy" for small stomachs; whatever milk and eggs a poor family can get are reserved for the father and for children over five. The youngest are thus deprived of proteins at the very time they need them most. Mothers, however, customarily give their children sweet, hot drinks called *atoles*, made by boiling ground-up corn in water, adding sugar, and flavoring the result with vanilla, anise, cinnamon or chocolate. The drink is tasty but has very low protein value. INCAP began advertising a better *atole* made in exactly the same way, but with Incaparina. The drink met with wide acceptance wherever people had the opportunity and the money to buy it.

To manufacture its product for general distribution, INCAP licensed private companies under strict quality and price controls. But to allow reasonable profits to the producers and retailers, the little plastic bags which contain enough Incaparina for three *atoles* (the nutritional equivalent of three glasses of milk) must be sold at four cents a bag. While far cheaper than milk, this remains too expensive for the average peasant family, which may have several children and a total cash income of $150 a year. It has been suggested, however, that with a subsidized plant and equipment, a nonprofit corporation could produce Incaparina for as little as one cent a bag.

Added together, all the protein-rich foods that could be made from the residues of cottonseed—and of peanuts, coconuts, soybeans and other crops—might satisfy one third of the world's present protein needs. In addition, scientists have suggested still more imaginative ways of increasing the supply.

In England, Dr. N. W. Pirie has pioneered in making protein supplements from leaves, and from such industrial by-products as the waste normally discarded while quick-freezing green peas. By means of special presses, he extracts from these materials a juicy substance which can be dried into a powder and added to almost any stew, sauce or biscuit. Some people have objected to its dark-green color, and Dr. Pirie has tried all kinds of recipes to make his leaf proteins attractive—from curry-flavored cocktail snacks to banana-flavored pastries for dessert—without arousing much enthusiasm. In an experiment conducted in Jamaica, however, babies, who were given no choice in the matter, thrived on half-and-half mixtures of milk and leaf-protein concentrate. Plans were promptly made to produce the concentrate in Jamaica, using leaves from the island's cane and cassava crops. In many tropical areas it might not even be necessary to utilize a cultivated crop to obtain leaf protein; the grasses and water hyacinths that proliferate in such climates could provide an almost inexhaustible supply.

Cheap new harvests from the sea

There are even more widespread sources of protein that have scarcely been tapped. The planned cultivation of fish, long practiced by the southern Chinese in their rice paddies, can produce large quantities of complete protein at far less cost than animal husbandry. Moreover, fish can be milled into an edible "flour," which can be preserved and shipped to areas where it is needed. In their search for protein, nutritionists are also considering plankton and other lower forms of aquatic life which exist in great abundance; seaweed and other algae, for example, are among the most prolific of all plants in the production of useful protein.

Finally, recent advances in the synthetic production of the amino acids themselves promise that the common grains—rice, wheat, corn—

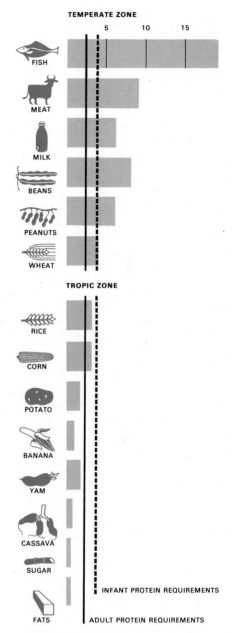

LACK OF PROTEIN is the most important cause of the malnutrition that affects perhaps one third of the world's population. In this chart, typical foods eaten by people living in temperate zones are contrasted with items of diet in tropic zones. The numbers at top indicate grams of protein per 100 calories of the various foods. As the vertical lines make plain, the tropic diet does not yield enough protein even for adults, and completely fails to meet the needs of infants.

can someday be made almost as valuable in protein content as steak. A small supplement of the missing amino acids can enormously increase the grain's protein value—a fact long appreciated by American farmers, who have been giving chickens such supplements in their feed since they became available commercially around 1950. It has been estimated that any one of the essential amino acids can be produced synthetically in quantity at less than one dollar per pound. At this price, enrichment of the common cereal grains might be feasible in most parts of the world.

A miraculous cure for scurvy

By such means, the worldwide protein shortage may someday be ended, just as the better-known vitamin deficiencies have been largely eliminated over the years. Until relatively recent times, for example, scurvy was a constant menace to armies and to the crews of sailing ships. Whenever people were cut off from fresh foods and dependent solely on preserved foodstuffs, this terrible disease found ready victims. Hippocrates gave a vivid description of scurvy's effects—bleeding gums, hemorrhaging and finally death—as early as the Fifth Century B.C. During the Crusades the disease became particularly widespread; in 1250 it forced the retreat and surrender of St. Louis with all his knights.

An early hint of a cure for scurvy is said to have come during one of Christopher Columbus' voyages to the New World. A handful of Portuguese sailors, desperately ill with the disease, asked to be left on an island they had sighted rather than die on shipboard and be thrown to the fish. While waiting for death on their island, the men ate some of its wild fruit and plants, and to their amazement began to recover. When Columbus' caravels passed by some months later on their way back to Europe, the pilot was astounded to see men waving from the land. As he approached, he found the sailors alive and healthy. The island of this miraculous recovery was later called Curaçao, from the Portuguese word for "cure."

In the 18th Century a British naval surgeon, James Lind, having heard of various remedies for scurvy, decided to try an experiment. There were numerous victims of the disease aboard his ship, and he divided a dozen of them into pairs and gave each pair a different kind of diet supplement, ranging from simple seawater to concoctions of herbs. Those who received oranges and lemons got well almost immediately. Eventually the crewmen of His Majesty's ships were given lime juice every day—earning them the nickname "limeys"—and scurvy never troubled the British Navy again.

By the early 20th Century it had been proved that this antiscurvy medicine—or antiscorbutic "principle"—could be found in other substances too—for example, in pine or spruce needles, which the Indians

FOOD FOR FISH AND MAN, some of the tiny sea life called plankton are shown greatly magnified. The diatoms *(far right)* are food for the other three kinds, which are eaten in turn by fish and thus end up indirectly in the diet of man. Plankton is so abundant in the ocean that it might become a vast direct source of food for humans if scientists could find a cheap way of harvesting it. Dry plankton contains as much as 59 per cent protein, and though it would not satisfy all nutritional requirements, it has been considered as a food supplement for people in developing nations where diets are protein-poor.

 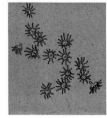  

HYDROZOA (POLYP AND MEDUSA) POLYCHAETA (BRISTLE WORMS)

of North America had long brewed into a tea to ward off disease. The "principle" is now known as ascorbic acid, or vitamin C, which exists abundantly not only in citrus fruits but also in vegetables such as cabbage and cauliflower. Since most diets now include fresh fruits and vegetables of some sort, scurvy is no longer the threat it once was. But it still crops up occasionally—for example, among improperly fed infants, among recluses who do not eat balanced diets, and among others who depend on canned goods which lack sufficient vitamin C.

Another common nutritional disease of past centuries was rickets, which resulted both from a deficient diet and lack of sunlight. In 17th Century England rickets was so prevalent as to pass for a normal state. Like most English children, young Charles I suffered from it, but his physician merely reported that the "joynts of his knees, hips and ankles, being great and loose, are not yet closed and knit together as it happeneth to many in their tender years." Rickets produces a softening of the bones, which then bend under the body's weight, causing bowlegs or knock-knees. In adults a related disease, osteomalacia, produces much pain, particularly in the spine or pelvis, as well as chronic fatigue.

In rickets, as in scurvy, practical experience pointed to cures long before medical science could explain why they worked. In the 19th Century cod-liver oil was used as both cure and preventive, to the disgust of generations of children who were forced to swallow it every day. The explanation came in 1919, when Sir Edward Mellanby proved the existence of an agent in cod-liver oil which was finally isolated and produced in 1931 as pure vitamin D. This vitamin, which increases the amount of calcium and phosphate deposited in the bones, may be found not only in fish oils but also in eggs, and in small quantities in butter and milk. It is also manufactured by the body when the sun's ultraviolet rays strike the skin. This is why in tropical areas rickets and osteomalacia are virtually unknown regardless of diet, afflicting only certain Moslem women and others who keep out of the sun.

Dr. Eijkman's limping chickens

Probably the most widespread of all vitamin-deficiency diseases today is beriberi. This disease, which once took several million lives each year in the Far East, still exacts a high toll in areas where people subsist largely on polished rice. It causes a painful degeneration of the nerves and, in extreme cases, can lead to paralysis or congestive heart failure. Its victims may sometimes be seen in Oriental countries crawling about on their hands, dragging their paralyzed legs behind them.

For a long time experts argued over whether beriberi was a contagious disease, or whether certain kinds of rice contained a toxic substance that was the cause of the ailment. One day in 1896 Dr. Christian Eijk-

CRUSTACEA (COPEPODS)   DIATOMS

man, a Dutch physician in Java, looked through the window of his hospital and noticed that some of the chickens in the yard were acting strangely. They limped, reeled along, and generally imitated the unsteady walk of the beriberi victims who filled the hospital. To confirm his suspicion that diet was responsible for their condition, Dr. Eijkman started a series of experiments—the first experiments to use animals to help solve problems of vitamin nutrition. He kept one group of limping chickens on the same diet of polished rice they had been getting as leftovers from patients' meals. Then he fed another group unpolished rice —and found that their symptoms disappeared. Some 30 years later, in 1926, the key nutritive element in rice hulls was identified as vitamin B_1, or thiamine, which is found in high concentration in cereals, nuts and yeast.

The attack on pellagra

The major deficiency disease in the U.S. was once pellagra. Characterized by ugly red splotches on the skin, digestive disorders and delirium, pellagra killed 10,000 persons a year in the Southern states alone just before World War I. Mississippi was the hardest hit; 1,192 persons died there from pellagra in 1914. The disease struck only the poor, and at first it was thought to be infectious. Later doctors believed that the only remedy was a diet rich in meat, milk or eggs, the very items the poor could least afford. But in 1938 it was shown that nicotinic acid, or niacin, could cure pellagra, as well as prevent it. Today bread, flour, cornmeal, macaroni and white rice are enriched with niacin (as well as other vitamins in the vitamin B complex, and iron) and pellagra is no longer a threat in the U.S. In other parts of the world, however, it has lost none of its potency. According to the World Health Organization, it still attacks 400,000 Egyptians every year.

There are other deficiency diseases which can afflict man when he does not get the right balance of foods: blindness from lack of vitamin A, still a frequent condition in Africa and the Far East; anemia from lack of iron, most common in children and in women of childbearing age; goiter from iodine deficiency. Still other nutritional diseases may go unrecognized. Scientists keep identifying new essential nutrients whose lack may cause damage, or discovering that previously unexplained deformities, such as one form of dwarfism, may be caused by a dietary deficiency of some mineral such as zinc.

Most of the classic deficiency diseases, however, have disappeared from the affluent world. They began to disappear even before nutritionists had defined the relationships between certain chemicals and health. As standards of living rose in Europe and North America, people ate not only more food but a wider variety of foods, helping to as-

THE DEFORMITIES OF RICKETS, caused by lack of sunshine and vitamin D, were first described in detail in 17th Century England by Francis Glisson, a medical professor, who called the disease rachitis, after the Greek word for "spine." The engraving above, the title page of Glisson's treatise, shows two rachitic children with humped backs caused by softening and bending of the spine. The listless child at right exhibits the typical knotty swelling and bowing of the legs.

sure better-balanced diets. This, along with more recent nutritional and medical knowledge, has been largely responsible for the increasing size of children in the Western nations. A similar increase in height is now taking place among Japanese children, as that nation's standard of living rises.

Overeating: deadly affliction

However, the very abundance of foods that has solved the nutritional problems of the past has produced its own new set of problems. In the U.S., obesity is the most common nutritional disorder today. It has been estimated that one out of five American men, and one out of four women, are 10 per cent or more overweight. Obesity is strongly linked with a shorter life expectancy and a higher susceptibility to atherosclerosis (the formation of lumpy deposits in the arteries), high blood pressure, diabetes and other ailments. Much attention in recent years has focused on obesity and atherosclerosis as causes of coronary heart disease, strokes and other serious vascular disorders. Since atherosclerotic heart disease alone accounts for some 20 per cent of deaths among U.S. adults, this is a serious indictment. It means that Americans may well be eating themselves to death.

An aging population of sedentary city-dwellers needs far fewer calories than a young one of frontiersmen and farmers, yet today's Americans continue to consume just as many calories as their ancestors, and frequently more. Not only do most people perform less physical labor to burn up these calories, but with well-heated buildings, elevators and better transportation of all kinds, they use less energy simply in living and getting around. At the same time they are surrounded by countless devices, from automobiles to electric can openers, which discourage even moderate exercise.

Besides consuming too many calories generally, modern men and women may be courting disease by overindulgence in certain essential foods. The poor man's starchy diet has been replaced by large quantities of fats, proteins and sugars—any of which, in excess, may be related to atherosclerosis and thus to coronary heart disease. For some years the popular villain has been fat, particularly the hard, saturated fats found in meat and butter. People who eat large quantities of these fats have been reported to have an increased level of cholesterol in their blood, and cholesterol in high concentrations has been linked statistically with atherosclerosis.

But research keeps illustrating the uncertainties of the arguments for excessive saturated fats as an invariable cause of coronary heart disease. For example, a study was carried out from 1955 through 1961 in the Pennsylvania town of Roseto, 95 per cent of whose 1,630 inhabitants

GRAINS OF RICE contain most of their vitamin value in their outer layers and embryo wall, as shown at left. But since rice spoils easily, it is usually highly milled and polished *(center)* to preserve it. This robs it of thiamine, or vitamin B₁. As a result, where polished rice is the staple food, as it is in most of Asia, people often get beriberi, a debilitating nutritional disease. To overcome this, rice can be parboiled *(right)*, "fixing" much of the thiamine into the grain.

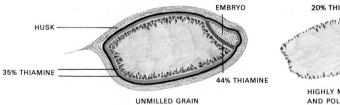

HUSK

EMBRYO

35% THIAMINE

44% THIAMINE

UNMILLED GRAIN

20% THIAMINE

HIGHLY MILLED
AND POLISHED

59% THIAMINE

PARBOILED AND MILLED

were descendants of a single group of Italian immigrants. The Rosetans were found to eat at least as much saturated fat as other Americans, consuming generous portions of ham, frying many foods in lard, and relishing every drop of gravy. Since they ate heavily and drank a great deal of wine, most of them were overweight. Yet during the years covered by the study, not a single Rosetan male under 47 died of a heart attack and even among older men the death rate from heart attacks was barely half that of neighboring towns. The explanation, according to the investigators, lay either in genetic factors or in the Rosetans' way of life: "gay, boisterous and unpretentious, mutually trusting (there is no crime in Roseto) and mutually supporting." Some Rosetans suggested that they simply did not worry much. In any case, when Rosetans have gone to live in big cities their rate of heart attacks has risen toward the U.S. norm.

It is only in the recent past that entire nations have had to worry about the diseases of surfeit. Around most of the world, deficient diets still remain a far greater problem. Doctors alone cannot bring health to children whose parents lack the means or education to provide them with the proper food. The diseases of starvation will disappear only when the cheap new products of science can be made available, and acceptable, to those who so desperately need them.

The Afflictions of Civilization

During recent decades, four diseases have startlingly risen to prominence as major health problems in the United States and Western Europe. Paradoxically, these prime killers and cripplers of the Western world—atherosclerosis, cancer, arthritis, and combined bronchitis and emphysema—owe a good deal of their present prominence to medicine's conquest of infectious diseases that once brought death at an early age. As life expectancy is prolonged, the diseases that chiefly afflict older people—as these four diseases do—become more important. Paradoxically, too, these afflictions are most prevalent in the most highly developed areas of the world. Rich diet, stress, smoking and the polluted atmosphere of industrialized societies appear to contribute variously to their development. How these diseases destroy is known. But how they originate and how they can be cured remain among the most urgent problems confronting modern medicine.

FOCUS ON FOUR ENIGMAS
Highlighted against the shadowed body of a man *(opposite)* are four mystery diseases. Each year, in the United States alone, atherosclerosis and cancer kill roughly a million people, while arthritis and combined bronchitis and emphysema add another half million new victims to the millions already disabled. More than $200 million is being spent annually to find causes and cures.

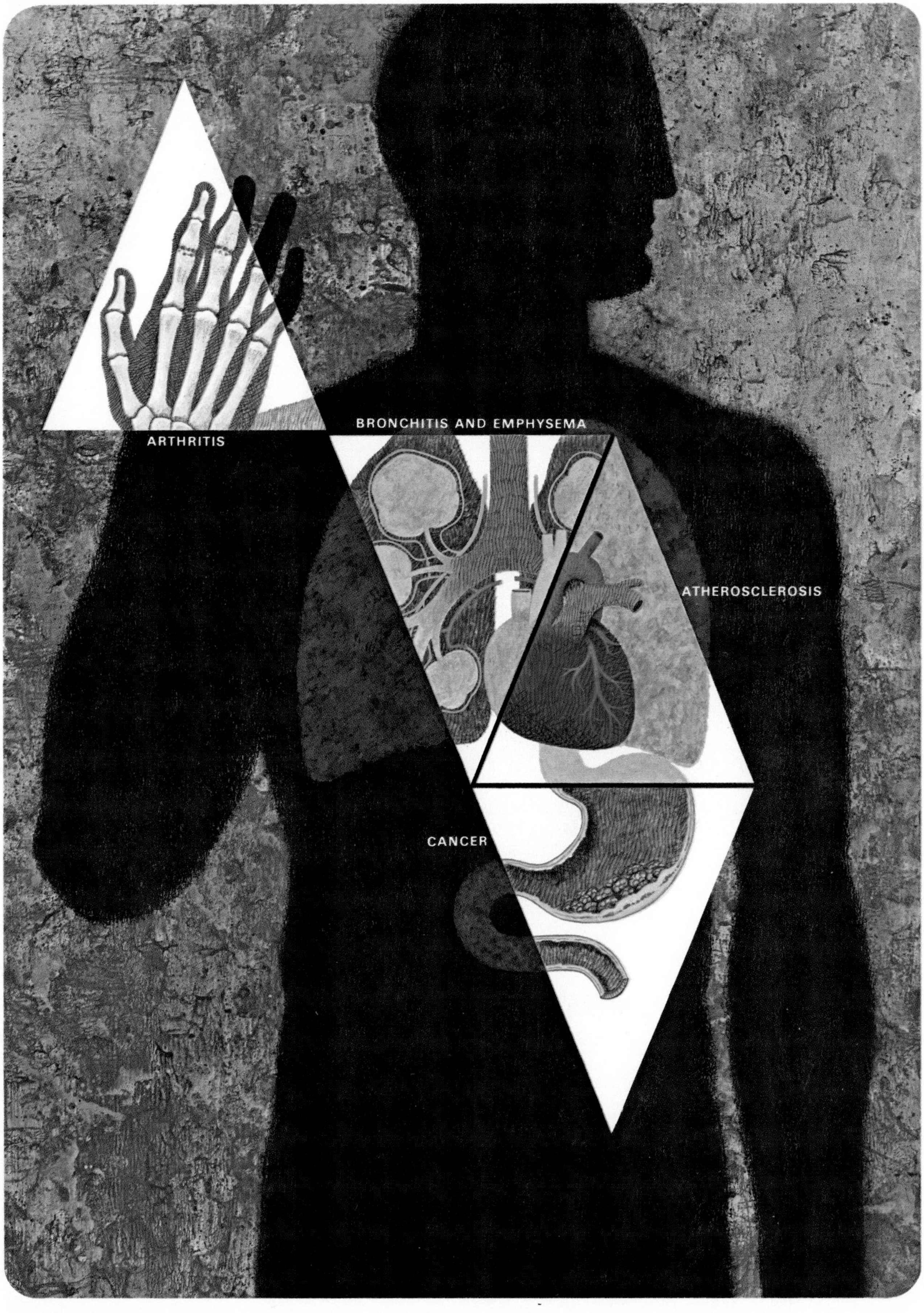

ARTHRITIS

BRONCHITIS AND EMPHYSEMA

ATHEROSCLEROSIS

CANCER

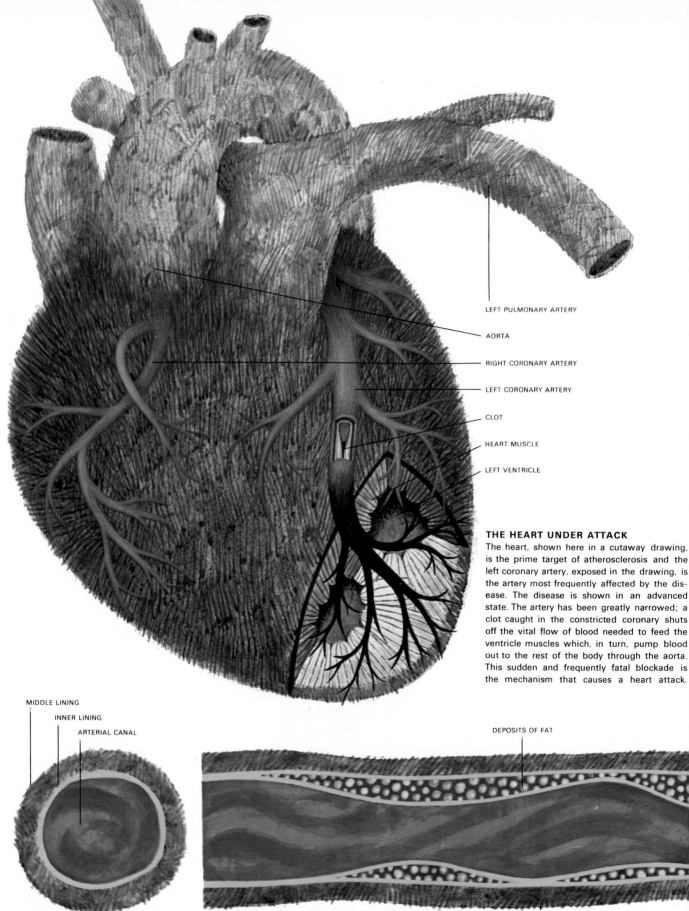

LEFT PULMONARY ARTERY

AORTA

RIGHT CORONARY ARTERY

LEFT CORONARY ARTERY

CLOT

HEART MUSCLE

LEFT VENTRICLE

THE HEART UNDER ATTACK

The heart, shown here in a cutaway drawing, is the prime target of atherosclerosis and the left coronary artery, exposed in the drawing, is the artery most frequently affected by the disease. The disease is shown in an advanced state. The artery has been greatly narrowed; a clot caught in the constricted coronary shuts off the vital flow of blood needed to feed the ventricle muscles which, in turn, pump blood out to the rest of the body through the aorta. This sudden and frequently fatal blockade is the mechanism that causes a heart attack.

MIDDLE LINING

INNER LINING

ARTERIAL CANAL

DEPOSITS OF FAT

A HEALTHY ARTERY

Open and flexible, a normal artery is free to expand and contract in response to the amount and rate of the pulsing blood flow. As fatty deposits, or atheromas, start to pile up along the inner lining, the artery narrows and begins to lose its healthy and essential elasticity.

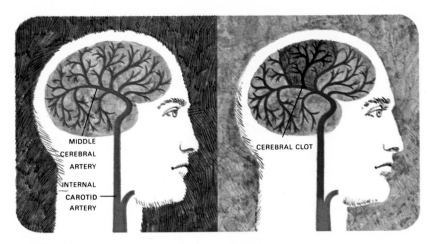

BLOCKING THE BRAIN

A stroke occurs when normal circulation of blood through the brain *(above, left)* is cut off by a clot *(right)*, usually in an atherosclerotic artery. Deprived of oxygen, brain cells perish and cease to exercise control over those parts of the body they normally direct. Damage to one side of the brain usually leads to loss of activity on the opposite side of the body.

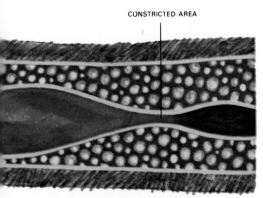

MAIN ATHEROSCLEROTIC SITES

Shown here are four key sections of the circulatory system in which atherosclerosis causes the severest damage. One reason these points are vital is that the brain, heart, kidneys and legs are each fed by single major arteries, and lack other sources of supply.

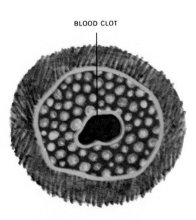

AN ATHEROSCLEROTIC ARTERY

Thickening deposits constrict the artery to a perilously narrow pathway. Hemmed in by stiffened walls, blood tends to stagnate and clot. The build-up of fat is a gradual process which usually becomes an acute problem only in persons of middle age or older.

Damming Vital Rivers of Blood

Atherosclerosis is the No. 1 killer among diseases in the U.S., claiming close to a million lives each year. A creeping killer, it is a disease of the arteries which becomes increasingly severe with age. Arteries afflicted with atherosclerosis gradually narrow and harden, as deposits of fat slowly build up within the elastic artery walls. Wherever arteries fork sharply, these dangerous layers tend to accumulate. After this has gone on for some time, the flow of blood is cramped *(below, left)*. Under such conditions, there is danger of clotting. Blood clots in atherosclerotic arteries are the cause of most coronary heart attacks *(opposite)* and cerebral strokes *(above, left)*. In the kidneys, clots cause tissue destruction; in the legs they may result in ulcers or gangrene.

The disabling effects of atherosclerosis and its prevalence among the aged made it appear an untreatable condition until comparatively recent times. It was not until the 1920s that a Chicago doctor convinced the medical profession that clots in the coronary artery caused many heart attacks and were thus presumably subject to therapy. Since then research into how atherosclerosis develops has advanced far, but its suspected causes *(pages 88, 89)* are still a subject of study and controversy.

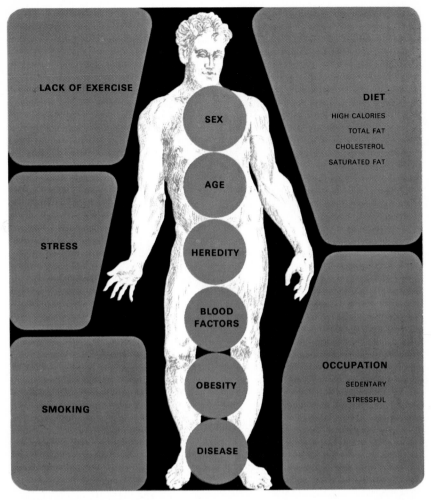

INTERACTING DANGER POINTS

The development of atherosclerosis depends on many linked factors, internal (within the figure) and external. Men are more susceptible than women, but this varies with age. The athero- sclerosis death rate of men 35 to 39 years old is 457 per cent higher than that of women in the same age group. Between 80 and 84, the male death rate is only 34 per cent higher.

A Complex of Causes

What causes atherosclerosis? Some experts, noting that the disease is as rare among undernourished popula- tions as it is common among people who overeat, believe that diet plays a major role. Others, emphasizing the fact that men are more prone to get the disease than women, think sex hormones may be a determining factor. Its frequency among business executives suggests to others that the disease is linked to the stresses of modern civilization.

No theory involving a single causa- tive agent has won widespread ac- ceptance among medical men. Most believe atherosclerosis is caused by many factors whose specific impor- tance varies from person to person. Thus, while diets with a high concen- tration of fatty substances almost certainly contribute to the disease, stress may speed its progress or he- reditary traits slow it. Atherosclero- sis is probably more of a threat to a sedentary office worker who eats too much and exercises too little than it is to a laborer who eats just as much but is physically active. One man's metabolized meat may well become the other's accumulation of poison.

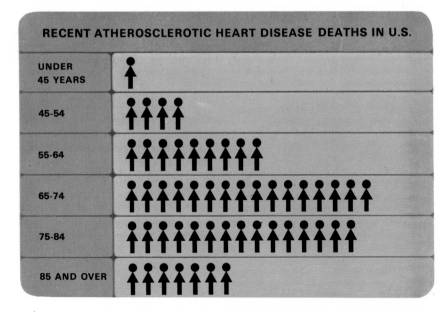

THE THREAT TO THE AGED

The chart *(left)* dramatically points up the high mortality rate of atherosclerosis among mid- dle-aged and older people. Each figure on the chart represents 10,000 people. In 1962 atherosclerosis was responsible for more than 40 per cent of all deaths in the United States.

TWO THEORIES OF HOW FATS ACCUMULATE IN ATHEROSCLEROSIS

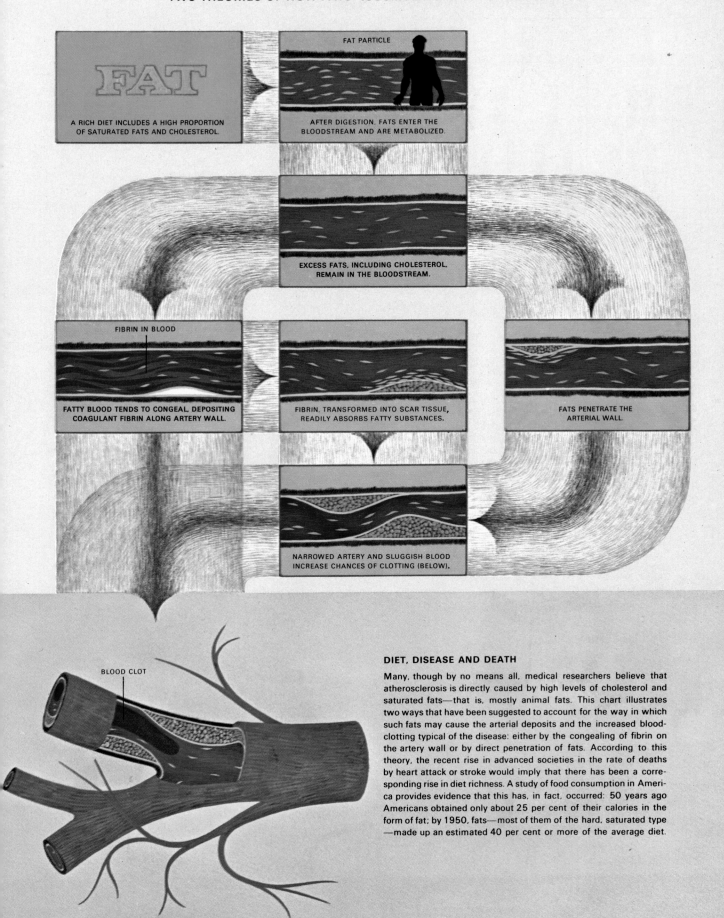

A RICH DIET INCLUDES A HIGH PROPORTION OF SATURATED FATS AND CHOLESTEROL.

FAT PARTICLE

AFTER DIGESTION, FATS ENTER THE BLOODSTREAM AND ARE METABOLIZED.

EXCESS FATS, INCLUDING CHOLESTEROL, REMAIN IN THE BLOODSTREAM.

FIBRIN IN BLOOD

FATTY BLOOD TENDS TO CONGEAL, DEPOSITING COAGULANT FIBRIN ALONG ARTERY WALL.

FIBRIN, TRANSFORMED INTO SCAR TISSUE, READILY ABSORBS FATTY SUBSTANCES.

FATS PENETRATE THE ARTERIAL WALL.

NARROWED ARTERY AND SLUGGISH BLOOD INCREASE CHANCES OF CLOTTING (BELOW).

BLOOD CLOT

DIET, DISEASE AND DEATH

Many, though by no means all, medical researchers believe that atherosclerosis is directly caused by high levels of cholesterol and saturated fats—that is, mostly animal fats. This chart illustrates two ways that have been suggested to account for the way in which such fats may cause the arterial deposits and the increased blood-clotting typical of the disease: either by the congealing of fibrin on the artery wall or by direct penetration of fats. According to this theory, the recent rise in advanced societies in the rate of deaths by heart attack or stroke would imply that there has been a corresponding rise in diet richness. A study of food consumption in America provides evidence that this has, in fact, occurred: 50 years ago Americans obtained only about 25 per cent of their calories in the form of fat; by 1950, fats—most of them of the hard, saturated type —made up an estimated 40 per cent or more of the average diet.

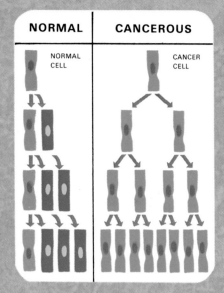

NORMAL	CANCEROUS
NORMAL CELL	CANCER CELL

DIVISION WITHOUT PURPOSE

Normal division of an unspecialized intestinal cell *(above, left)* produces specialized cells that are used to line the intestine. Cancerous cells *(right)* proliferate rapidly, producing more and more of their own kind. Thus tumors are formed that damage the organ in which they arise.

Cancer: Anarchy of the Body's Cells

Cancer, the second-ranking fatal disease in America, accounts for one out of every six deaths in the United States. Although older people, especially those over 40, are most threatened by cancer, it can attack people of any age. Indeed, one form of the disease, leukemia, is most prevalent among children. No organ or tissue is safe from this attack, although some *(opposite, top left)* are more susceptible than others.

Preliminary stages in the development of various types of cancer may take a number of years as, for example, in lung cancer *(below)*. However, once any cell or group of cells has finally become cancerous, multiplication and growth are swift. Unlike normal cells *(far left)*, which regenerate cells with specialized functions, cancerous cells produce cells whose specialized function has been eclipsed by a powerful, primitive drive for unrestrained proliferation. Eventually this process forms a mass of malignant tissue called a tumor.

Malignant tumors grow in many pernicious ways. Most commonly they damage other cells by physically crowding them and by grabbing an excessive share of nutrients. A greater danger is that the initial tumor may spread to other areas. Localized, a tumor may be treated or removed. But when diseased cells have found their way into the bloodstream *(opposite, top right)*, the cancer spreads and ultimately becomes impossible either to treat or control.

LUNG CANCER: FIRST STAGE

The normal lining of an air passage in the lung *(below, left)* consists of a layer of outer (epithelial) cells supported by a mosaic of inner (basal) cells underlain by the basilar membrane. Excessive multiplication of basal cells *(below, right)* is an early stage of lung cancer.

LUNG CANCER: SECOND STAGE

In a further development, tough, scarlike (squamous) cells replace epithelial cells along the surface of the air passage. These capsule-shaped cells form as a response to chronic local irritation. Underlying basal cells have reverted to their previous normal growth rate.

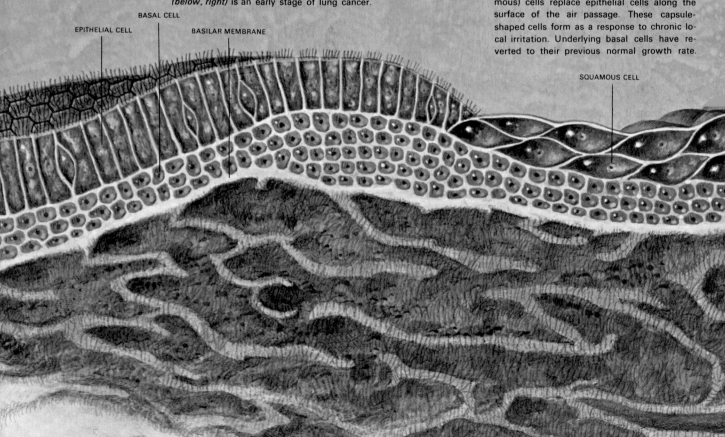

BASAL CELL

EPITHELIAL CELL

BASILAR MEMBRANE

SQUAMOUS CELL

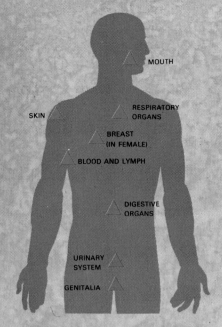

VULNERABLE CANCER SITES

Cancer may strike anywhere in the body, but certain regions (marked by triangles in the diagram) are especially vulnerable. In men, the lungs and digestive tract are the most frequently affected sites; in women, the danger spots are the breast, digestive tract and the cervix.

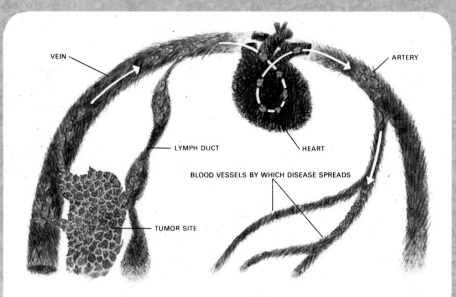

BLOOD ROUTES TO NEW SITES

The most insidious aspect of most cancers is their ability to spread out from a localized site like a tumor *(above, left)* to other regions of the body. The bloodstream is the carrier. The tumor in this diagram could spread by means of cells directly invading a nearby vein or by cells growing through the lymphatic duct to reach a vein and lodge elsewhere in the body.

LUNG CANCER: THIRD STAGE

In the final stage before the actual outbreak of cancerous growth, basal cells once again multiply. Now, however, these cells appear to have taken on a changed character. Some, as indicated by the reddish coloring below, may already have had their genetic structure altered.

LUNG CANCER: FOURTH STAGE

The actual cancer begins as a localized phenomenon within the basal cells. Eventually the diseased cells, if untreated, replace the squamous cells above and invade the connective tissues beneath. At this stage, the disease is so advanced that the victim may be doomed.

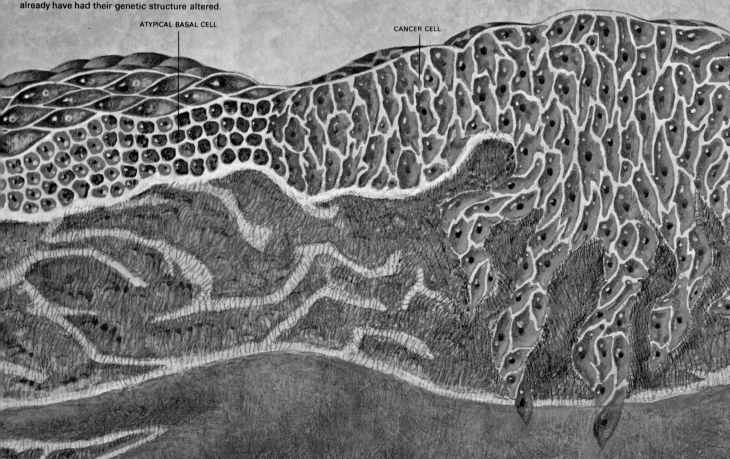

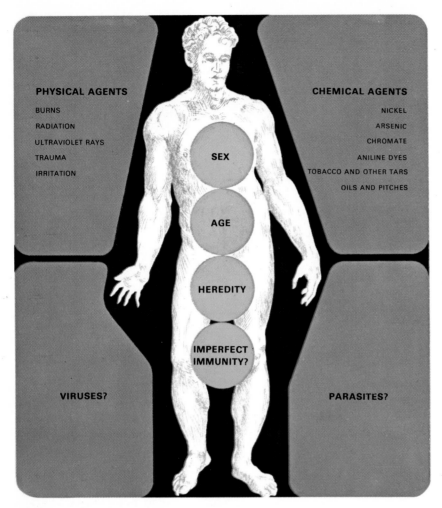

PHYSICAL AGENTS

BURNS
RADIATION
ULTRAVIOLET RAYS
TRAUMA
IRRITATION

SEX

AGE

HEREDITY

IMPERFECT IMMUNITY?

CHEMICAL AGENTS

NICKEL
ARSENIC
CHROMATE
ANILINE DYES
TOBACCO AND OTHER TARS
OILS AND PITCHES

VIRUSES?

PARASITES?

THE MYSTERIOUS SOURCES OF CANCER
Within the figure are some internal factors that may contribute to cancer; around the figure are some known external cancer-inducing agents. Viruses and parasites are only suspected. Others, such as cigarette smoking, are indicated by powerful circumstantial evidence: people who smoke two packs or more daily are 60 times more likely to get lung cancer than nonsmokers.

Cancer: The Body's Malignant Mystery

What is it that causes a normal cell to begin the process of abnormal reproduction called cancer? The earliest partial answer to this urgent and baffling question was provided by an 18th Century London doctor, Percival Pott, who related the high rate of scrotal cancer among chimney sweeps to some cancer-inducing agent in soot. Since Pott's time many such agents have been identified. Excessive exposure to radiation or certain industrial dyes is known to induce, if not actually cause, cancer in both animals and man. Chemicals found in automobile exhaust, industrial smog and cigarette smoke have been implicated in lung cancer.

A renewed interest in the idea that viruses may cause human cancer has been aroused by new techniques that demonstrate convincingly that viruses cause animal leukemia. Certain viruses have also been discovered that produce a variety of tumors in animals. A common virus which causes human respiratory disease has been shown to produce cancer in animals. Under the circumstances, the conclusion seems inescapable that a relationship exists between viruses and at least some human cancers.

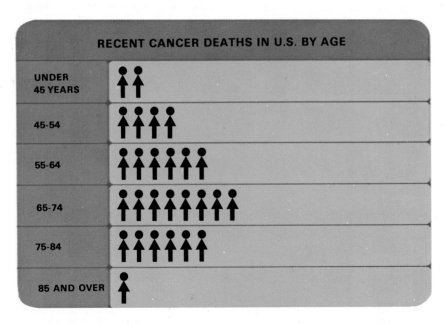

RECENT CANCER DEATHS IN U.S. BY AGE

UNDER 45 YEARS	
45-54	
55-64	
65-74	
75-84	
85 AND OVER	

A PRESENT AND FUTURE MENACE
Cancer most frequently strikes down people between the late fifties and early eighties, as the chart at left shows. One figure represents 10,000 persons. Unless there is a breakthrough in prevention, one out of every four Americans will have the disease during his lifetime.

92

HOW A CANCER VIRUS MIGHT TAKE OVER

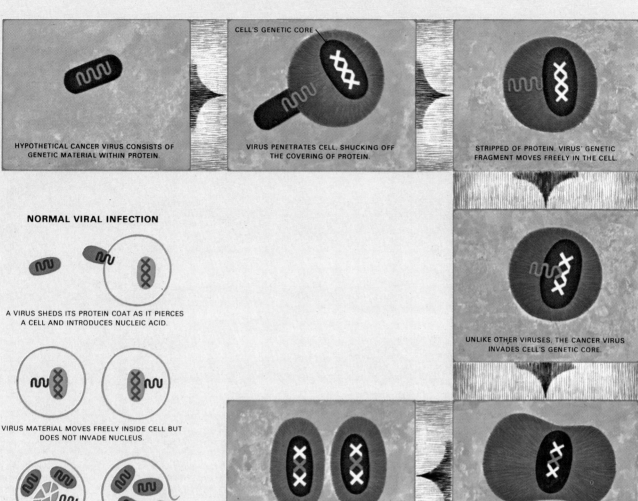

HYPOTHETICAL CANCER VIRUS CONSISTS OF GENETIC MATERIAL WITHIN PROTEIN.

CELL'S GENETIC CORE

VIRUS PENETRATES CELL, SHUCKING OFF THE COVERING OF PROTEIN.

STRIPPED OF PROTEIN, VIRUS' GENETIC FRAGMENT MOVES FREELY IN THE CELL.

UNLIKE OTHER VIRUSES, THE CANCER VIRUS INVADES CELL'S GENETIC CORE.

CELL DIVISION NOW PRODUCES UNSPECIALIZED, MALIGNANT CELLS.

CELLULAR GENETIC CONTROL IS ALTERED BY THE INVASION OF THE VIRUS.

NORMAL VIRAL INFECTION

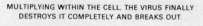

A VIRUS SHEDS ITS PROTEIN COAT AS IT PIERCES A CELL AND INTRODUCES NUCLEIC ACID.

VIRUS MATERIAL MOVES FREELY INSIDE CELL BUT DOES NOT INVADE NUCLEUS.

MULTIPLYING WITHIN THE CELL, THE VIRUS FINALLY DESTROYS IT COMPLETELY AND BREAKS OUT.

TYPICAL MALIGNANT TUMOR

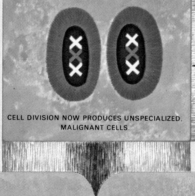

VIRUSES AND CANCER

Whether or not the "cancer virus" shown at work in the diagram above can actually cause tumors in humans is not known. But the quest for proof is occupying hundreds of researchers in scores of laboratories. Already a dozen viruses have been established as definite causes of cancer in animals. But following the trail of the virus within the cell is an exasperatingly difficult task. In one type of rabbit tumor, the virus cannot be detected when the tumor is growing most actively—but is readily observable in old cells, where the damage has already been done. This reverses the pattern found in normal viral infections, where the organisms are most easily detectable under the electron microscope as an illness reaches its peak. The elusive behavior of cancer-causing viruses in animals may explain why they have never been found in human tumors. By the time the tumor has grown large enough to be detected, some experts speculate, the virus has lost its own identity by merging with the nucleic acids of infected cells. To further complicate the picture, other researchers suggest that there may be no specific cancer-inducing virus. Rather, they say, under the right conditions, *any* virus may invade a cell, alter its genetic structure and initiate the rampant cellular reproduction that is known as cancer.

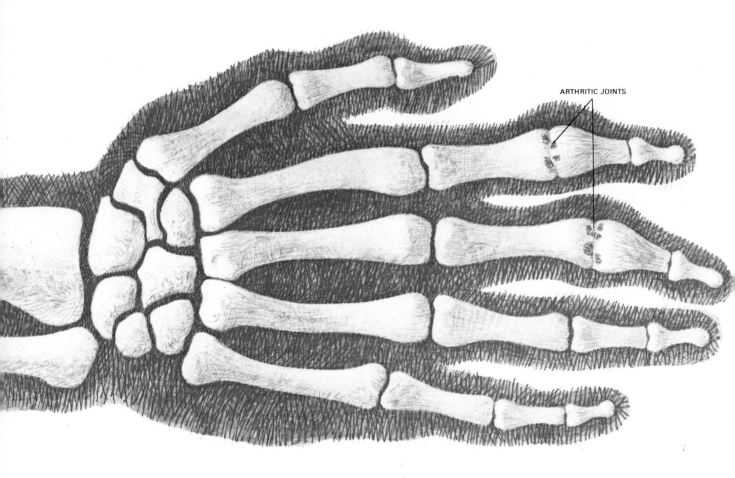

ARTHRITIC JOINTS

FINGERS FROZEN IN PLACE

Typical results of rheumatoid arthritis appear in two finger joints of the right hand. ("Arthritis" is a combination of Greek words meaning "joint" and "inflammation.") The second joints are a favorite target of the disease, but other finger joints and the wrist, too, may be affected. As explained in detail by the drawings below, the disease damages tissue and bone, causing the joint to swell painfully. Eventually the joint may deteriorate so much that it is immobilized in the knobby, misshapen deformity that is characteristic of advanced cases of rheumatoid arthritis.

BONE   SYNOVIAL MEMBRANE   JOINT CAPSULE

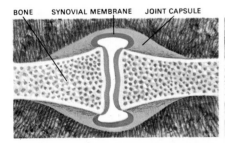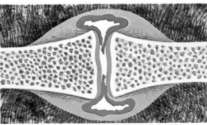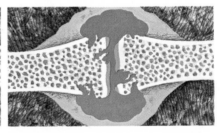

Shown above are three progressive stages of rheumatoid-arthritic attack in a joint; below, each phase is shown in greater detail.

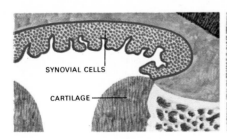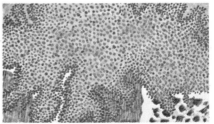

SYNOVIAL CELLS

CARTILAGE

A TISSUE GONE WRONG

A normal finger joint, shown in the pictures above, is lined with synovial membrane, which secretes fluid to lubricate the joint. Rheumatoid arthritis upsets the normal function of synovial cells, inducing them to multiply at an unnatural rate, which causes swelling. The synovial tissue creeps into the joint itself, as shown in the center picture. In late stages of the disease *(right)*, the synovial membrane packs the joint, and the unhealthy tissue eats away the cartilage covering the ends of the bones and even erodes the bone itself, rendering the joint useless.

The Greatest Crippler

Arthritis, afflicting at least 12 million Americans, is this country's chief cause of physical disability. This group of diseases appears in many forms. One is old-fashioned gout; more prevalent is osteoarthritis, which produces the aches and hobbled joints of old age; and the form most feared is rheumatoid arthritis (shown on these pages), which often attacks young adults and persists into advanced age.

Arthritis strikes body joints or connective tissues with painful and disabling effect (*opposite*). But why it attacks and how it can be prevented are unanswered. One theory having to do with rheumatoid arthritis surmises that the body literally turns on itself, as illustrated at right. Though doctors can ease the pain and curb the damage, they are still a long way from controlling the great crippler.

ONE THEORY ON THE CAUSE OF RHEUMATOID ARTHRITIS

SYNOVIAL CELL.

A CELL IN THE SYNOVIAL MEMBRANE IS DAMAGED BY INFECTION.

ANTIBODY

ANTIBODIES ARE PRODUCED BY THE BODY IN RESPONSE TO THE DAMAGE.

ANTIBODIES, UNABLE TO RECOGNIZE HEALTHY CELLS, ATTACK THEM TOO.

ANTIBODY DESTROYS DAMAGED CELL. A NORMAL BODY REACTION.

OTHER CELLS START DIVIDING TO REPLACE DAMAGED CELLS.

NEW CELLS FORM IN SYNOVIAL TISSUE.

SYNOVIAL TISSUE

AS SYNOVIAL TISSUE PROLIFERATES. OVERGROWTH DISABLES JOINT.

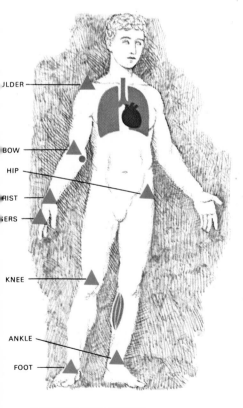

SHOULDER —
ELBOW —
HIP —
WRIST —
FINGERS —
KNEE —
ANKLE —
FOOT —

TARGETS FOR ATTACK
Many of the body's joints are vulnerable to arthritic affliction, as shown above. Rheumatoid arthritis can also cause a painful inflammation of muscles, and may scar the lungs and heart.

AN ASSAULT ON THE CELLS
One theory of the cause of rheumatoid arthritis, the autoimmune theory, is illustrated here. Antibodies usually attack only abnormal cells or foreign substances, living or dead. But the autoimmune theory suggests that antibodies in synovial tissue sometimes attack healthy cells as well, causing them to multiply in response to injury. Swelling and joint damage is the result.

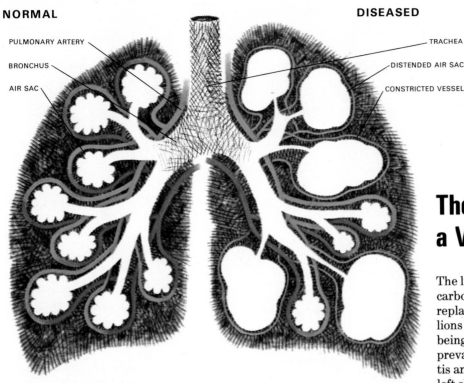

NORMAL   DISEASED

PULMONARY ARTERY ─────   ───────── TRACHEA

BRONCHUS ─────   ─── DISTENDED AIR SAC

AIR SAC ───   ── CONSTRICTED VESSEL

A DANGEROUS INFLATION

The effects of bronchitis and emphysema are shown in this schematic drawing of greatly enlarged air sacs of the human lung. In a normal lung, clusters of these tiny sacs collectively provide a large surface for respiration, and the bronchial tubes permit free passage of air. In the diseased lung, the membranes of the individual sacs have broken down, forming large sacs with much less surface area. Also the bronchial tubes and blood vessels are constricted.

The New Threat to a Vital Function

The lung's job is to remove excessive carbon dioxide from the blood and replace it with fresh oxygen. For millions of people that vital exchange is being threatened by an increasingly prevalent enemy: combined bronchitis and emphysema. The drawings at left show how the disease attacks the tiny air sacs within the lungs. In some victims the lung damage causes mere shortness of breath; in others, death may result.

The most striking fact about combined bronchitis and emphysema is how rapidly it is spreading through Western societies. Relatively rare 25 years ago, it is now the No. 1 respiratory ailment and afflicts nearly 10 million Americans. Doctors have a lot to learn about its causes and the sequence of its effects *(opposite)*, but they do know that cigarette smoke and polluted air are seriously implicated and that bronchitis and emphysema are therefore another unwelcome by-product of modern life.

NORMAL   DISEASED

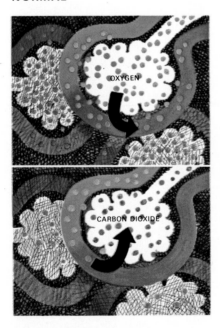
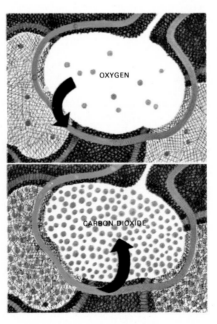

A POISONOUS BOTTLENECK

The exchange of gases which occurs in respiration—the intake of oxygen and the output of carbon dioxide—is shown here in greatly magnified scale. In a normal lung, oxygen enters the air sac *(top left)* and passes readily through the membrane into the bloodstream, while carbon dioxide passes from the blood into the air sac *(bottom left)*. In the diseased lung, very little oxygen can get into the air sac because of the constriction of the air passage *(top right)*, while carbon dioxide accumulates in the expanded sac at an increased rate *(bottom right)*.

A DEADLY CYCLE IN THE LUNGS

Since emphysema is almost always associat with bronchitis, many doctors think the disea starts with a bronchial infection which th constricts passages leading to the air sacs *(l arrow, opposite)*. It might be, however, that sequence is reversed—that emphysema fi dilates the air sacs, and that their expansi then causes bronchial constriction and collap *(right arrow)*. Whatever the direction of the cle, bronchitis and emphysema can have dr tic, far-reaching effects. In severe cases, lack oxygen produces brain damage, and enlarg and weakens a heart which is forced to w harder pumping blood through diseased lun

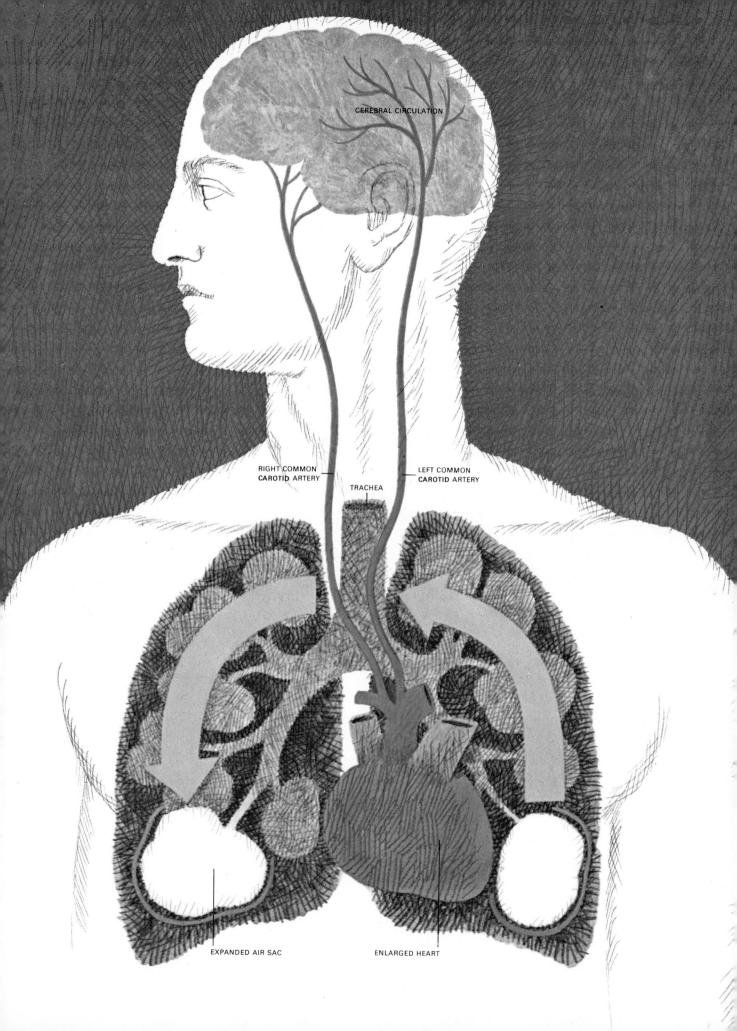

CEREBRAL CIRCULATION

RIGHT COMMON
CAROTID ARTERY

LEFT COMMON
CAROTID ARTERY

TRACHEA

EXPANDED AIR SAC

ENLARGED HEART

5
The Insidious Poisons

A PERVASIVE CHEMICAL
The head of suds that threatens to engulf the walkway of this sewage-treatment tank betrays the presence in the water of a chemical foaming agent used in most detergents. Though this chemical is not known to be harmful, it is—like many identifiable poisons dumped into U.S. water systems—extremely persistent, passing through treatment plants almost unaltered.

IN THE PAST FEW DECADES man has created an astonishing health problem for himself: in many parts of the world he is now regularly ingesting small amounts of poisons. He has polluted the atmosphere so heavily that much of the population now breathes a mixture of highly toxic gases with every lungful of air. He has allowed lethal insecticides and weed killers to contaminate his water—a resource from which they cannot be removed by any known method. In his effort to combat disease he has created hundreds of drugs that act powerfully on the entire body; each year some of them are demonstrated to be toxic for human beings in ways never suspected when they were marketed. In effect he has surrounded himself with a new kind of filth which may breed disease as effectively in the long run as the microbial filth of 19th Century slums.

Industrial societies are exposing themselves to these man-made poisons in almost total ignorance of their possible delayed or cumulative effects. Often in the past man has ingested strange substances for years in the supposition that they were harmless, only to find later that their effects were harmful—sometimes lethal—over a period of time. The dangers of cigarette smoking are now well publicized, but the statistical evidence of the effect of smoking on health became apparent only some 40 years after the habit had become widespread and fashionable. After World War I, radium was added to pep tonics and advertised as a cure for tiredness and arthritis. It was also used to make luminous paint. Some of the first workers hired to paint luminous watch dials habitually pointed their brushes by twirling them between their lips. Some of them died of radium poisoning within a few years; more than 40 others died of bone cancer over a period of 30 years. Most had swallowed only a minute speck of radium in all. The Atomic Energy Commission is still sponsoring detailed studies of people who have swallowed radium from various sources, since they provide some of the few available examples of the long-range effects of small, repeated doses of radiation on man.

Of all the toxic chemicals men are now regularly and involuntarily exposed to, the strange mixture that passes for city air is probably causing the greatest concern to the largest number of people. Every human being depends on the 15,000 quarts of air he breathes each day—yet man persists in using the sky as a garbage pail. He began to introduce smoke into the air with his first fire. The volume of soot and smoke increased markedly with the advent of soft coal and the birth of industrial cities—and by World War II air pollution was becoming severe. In the years since then, the volume of pollutants in city air has increased faster than ever, while their nature has changed for the worse. Old-fashioned coal and low-grade fuel oil still send soot and sulfur dioxide into the air; now petroleum refineries, chemical industries and automobiles add vast quantities of other toxic gases and fumes—some of them particularly insidious because they are unaccompanied by soot and odors.

By the middle of this century, air pollution had reached such concentrations that industrial cities began to be plagued by the now-familiar phenomenon known as "smog." The word is a contraction of "smoke" and "fog," but smog often contains substances far more dangerous than smoke, and it does not even require the presence of fog. What it does require is a stationary mass of air in which pollutants can accumulate. This happens when the air near the earth is colder than the air above it and thus does not rise—an upside-down meteorological situation called a thermal inversion.

An epic dose of poison

A number of historic "killer" smogs have made it plain that a single city's ordinary volume of pollutants may be not merely toxic but lethal when they are concentrated in one epic dose. In 1948 a three-day thermal inversion hung over an industrial valley that included the small city of Donora, Pennsylvania. Under the tight lid of air, a zinc-reduction plant, a steel mill and other factories continued full tilt, pouring sulfur dioxide and other gases into the chilly, stagnant fog. When sulfur dioxide is exposed to moisture it turns into sulfuric acid—a substance potent enough to corrode metal. By the third day, 5,910 persons were ill—43 per cent of the population. Complaints included shortness of breath, nausea, diarrhea, coughs and sore throats. In a period that should statistically have seen no more than two deaths, 20 persons died, most of them of respiratory and heart diseases.

The most devastating smog ever recorded occurred in London in 1952. In early December of that year a sooty fog settled over the city, reducing visibility to near zero. The fog lasted four days, and experienced Londoners stayed home as much as possible—all but doctors and nurses, who were exceptionally busy attending large numbers of respiratory cases. By the fourth day of the fog, hundreds of patients suffering from pneumonia, bronchitis and heart disease had crowded the city's hospitals, and still more were waiting for beds. It was not until some time after the fog had cleared that the public—and even the medical profession—fully realized the size of the disaster. During the week of the fog and the week that immediately followed, London's normal death rates had been exceeded by 4,000.

Unlike these rare, acute episodes in which a sooty smog obscures the sun, many American smogs are barely visible except as a haze seen from a distance, and they occur much more frequently than is commonly thought. They consist largely of petroleum by-products that have been exposed to sunlight, and their chief contributor is the automobile. Every thousand cars crawling through congested urban streets daily discharge into the air about 3.2 tons of carbon monoxide, 400 to 800 pounds of hydrocarbon vapors, and 100 to 300 pounds of nitrogen oxides, plus smaller amounts of other chemicals, some of which have produced cancer in laboratory animals. Carbon monoxide is lethal when breathed in high concentrations. The hydrocarbons and nitrogen oxides at first give little sign of their presence, but after an hour or so in the sunshine they begin to undergo alarming "photochemical" reactions—that is, reactions due to light. They form new compounds which irritate the eyes and mucous membranes. If a thermal inversion is present, they collect as a thin, grayish haze—a photochemical smog.

As the number of automobiles increases and as nations grow more industrialized and urbanized, the danger of air pollution becomes greater. The deaths in Donora and London coincided conspicuously with acute smogs, and they could be counted. But nobody knows how many other people die each year from the delayed or cumulative effects of breathing chronically polluted air.

Most city air contains both sulfur dioxide and the products of photochemical smog. Together they make a potent chemical brew. The wastes from automobiles wither vegetation; they have caused the loss of millions of dollars' worth of crops in California alone. The sulfur dioxide puts runs in nylon stockings, corrodes metals and eats stonemasonry. The façades of city buildings everywhere are pitted and black with grime. The ruins of Athens and Rome are believed to have deteriorated more in this century than in the previous 500 years.

The high cost of breathing

At the same time, chronic ailments of the respiratory tract have become much more widespread. In the U.S., the death rate from lung cancer among males increased eightfold between 1930 and 1960. The death rates from pulmonary emphysema increased four times between 1950 and 1959. The incidence of these diseases correlates closely with the presence of chronically polluted air, just as it does with inhaling cigarette smoke—a portable form of air pollution. And there is no medical doubt that heavy concentrations of pollutants aggravate the condition of persons with diseased hearts and lungs, sometimes fatally. In every killer smog, the highest toll is among heart and lung patients.

In spite of the high correlation between the presence of pollutants and the incidence of certain diseases, most urban areas have done remarkably little to control pollution. Chemical plants, power generators, incinerators and automobiles continue to toss their refuse into the air. In 1961, only 17 states were spending as much as $5,000 a year for pollution control. The amount spent by local agencies in the nation was only about eight million dollars. Of this, $3.4 million was spent by one locality: Los Angeles.

Los Angeles' eye-stinging photochemical smogs have won an unenviable reputation from coast to coast. Thermal inversions are particularly frequent in Southern California, where layers of high, warm air drift in from the Pacific—and Los Angeles, at once sunny and hemmed in by mountains on three sides, is especially vulnerable to their effects. The city grew rapidly during World War II; so did the volume of pollutants in the air. In September of 1943, the city experienced its first severe smog. Eyes streaming and throats sore, residents flooded newspaper and government offices with anxious calls. Since then, smog has become a way of life in Los Angeles; the city is afflicted with a noticeable haze about 100 days out of every year.

Stern measures in Los Angeles

Almost alone among U.S. communities, Los Angeles has been galvanized by its acute problem into taking adequate measures. In 1947, the area established a pollution-control authority whose first step was to enforce stern regulations over industrial smoke and fumes. Next, it passed an ordinance prohibiting homeowners from burning trash in backyards—effectively eliminating some 500 tons of pollutants that rose into the air from 1.5 million fires every day. All of this whitened the smog, but did relatively little to reduce it.

Working together with the state, Los Angeles officials then took up the toughest problem, the automobile. Unburned petroleum products in the form of gases and vapors not only leave the tail pipes of automobiles, but also leak out from crankcases, carburetors and fuel tanks. Under threat of California legislation, the automobile industry installed devices called "blow-bys" on all 1961-model cars sold in the state. Blow-bys run gases that have leaked into the crankcase back through the engine for burning. In 1962 the industry made blow-bys standard in all new cars sold in the U.S.

But blow-bys eliminate only about a quarter of the total hydrocarbon vapors that escape from automobiles into the air. California also declared its intention of setting even more stringent standards for cars operating in the state, and asked industry to develop devices that would complete the oxidation of petroleum products before they leave tail pipes. In 1964, when the state approved four models of exhaust-control devices, it made them obligatory on all new cars sold in California beginning with 1966 models, and on older cars shortly thereafter. Theoretically, such devices, together with blow-bys, eliminate about 80 per cent of the hydrocarbons and 60 per cent of the carbon monoxide discharged by automobiles.

POLLUTION from automobiles, a major cause of air contamination, is largely eliminated by the use of the two devices diagramed below. The blow-by recycler carries unburned fuel from the crankcase back through the firing cycle a second time. Even more effective is the afterburner. Unburned fuel and exhaust gases pass through a chamber near the end of the exhaust system. There, air is introduced and a spark plug ignites the mixture, changing it to harmless carbon dioxide and water.

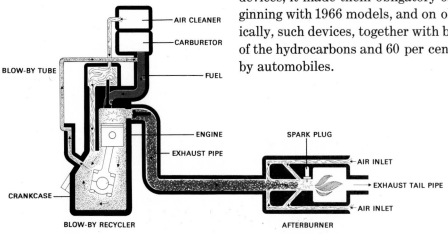

AIR CLEANER
CARBURETOR
BLOW-BY TUBE
FUEL
ENGINE
SPARK PLUG
EXHAUST PIPE
AIR INLET
EXHAUST TAIL PIPE
AIR INLET
CRANKCASE
BLOW-BY RECYCLER
AFTERBURNER

As long as civilization gets most of its heat and power from coal and petroleum, however, no amount of smoke traps or exhaust controls seems likely to succeed in keeping the air really clean in huge, congested urban centers. Some health officials believe there is only one long-range solution: the development of some power source that creates little or no air pollution—perhaps atomic energy, or even tidal energy or solar energy. In the meantime, they propose an immediate switch to electrified urban mass transport.

Thus far, the greatest progress in clearing the atmosphere has been in the reduction of atomic fallout. In 1963, the U.S., Great Britain and the Soviet Union agreed to stop the atmospheric testing of nuclear devices, which had been spreading radioactive dust over the Northern Hemisphere since 1945. As a result, the volume of dangerous strontium 90 and cesium 137 reaching the earth began to decline at last in 1964. But it is expected to continue falling in decreasing amounts for several decades, even if all the world's nuclear powers—including such countries as France and Communist China, which did not sign the test-ban agreement—refrain from further tests.

The contamination of water probably affects as many people as the contamination of air. Man has been dumping wastes into handy streams since time began. New York City still deposits half a billion gallons of sewage a day into the East and Hudson Rivers. But sewage decomposes fairly rapidly, and its germs can be killed by chemical treatment. Far more alarming is the variety of new, long-lived chemicals which resist all purification processes. A research center in Cincinnati attempted in 1960 to make a count of all the identifiable chemicals in U.S. waters, and reached the figure of 100—detergents, insecticides, weed killers, solvents—before giving up. Said one researcher, "We believe that for every one we've found, we have missed hundreds of others."

Cool, clear, poisoned water

Many of these chemicals in waterways are known poisons. Some are dumped into streams as industrial wastes. Some are deliberately applied to water to control certain kinds of plants or fish. Still others drain in after rains from land treated with pesticides.

These poisons may be diluted in waterways to concentrations as low as a fractional part per billion, and no human being is known to have died from drinking water contaminated with them. But fish have been killed by them in large numbers. Mississippi River fish have been dying by the millions every winter since 1960. Their bodies become grotesquely bloated, and they make a gruesome spectacle as they surface by the thousands and flop convulsively about, unable to submerge. An estimated five million fish died in this manner in 1964, some of them tough patriarchs of the river, weighing as much as 150 pounds each. Dead shrimp, crabs, water birds and even otters and mink were found near the mouth of the river. Seeking the cause of this carnage, U.S. Public Health Service chemists identified a number of pesticides, including DDT, in the blood of the dead fish. These pesticides had been used increasingly on local crops. Further investigation specifically incriminated endrin, a highly toxic pesticide. Endrin was entering the river in relatively large amounts from a sewer connected to an endrin-manufacturing plant in Memphis, Tennessee, and further amounts were draining in from the fields. Highly refined testing techniques showed that endrin was present in New Orleans drinking water, although at the very low level of .025 parts per billion. It had evidently made a long journey downstream, entering the water supply of all the communities along the way that used Mississippi River water.

Human beings consume pesticides not only in water but also in seafood, fruit, vegetables, milk and many other items in the diet. Scientists are now concerned about the accumulation of these poisons in the human system. Endrin, DDT and other pesticides settle in body fat, where they persist for years. As long as they stay in the fat, they do no apparent harm. But any rapid weight loss may release a dangerous flow of these poisons into the bloodstream. Scientists reason that the Mississippi fish died in the winter because they burned up extra-large amounts of body fat.

In 1962 the best-selling book *Silent Spring,* by biologist Rachel Carson, aroused widespread controversy by predicting that continued use of pesticides would lead to disasters ranging from the death of birds to the total upsetting of the ecology of nature. Many authorities suspect that she overstated the dangers. In any case, the damage caused by pesticides must be weighed against their very definite benefits. According to one evaluation by the World Health Organization, it would be impossible to feed the world's growing population without the use of pesticides. Nevertheless, since *Silent Spring* appeared, research into less dangerous means of coping with insects has accelerated, and indiscriminate spraying with poisonous chemicals has declined.

Medicines that cause sickness

Another group of potent chemicals that is now being eyed with reservations by scientists is the array of modern drugs. New medicines are being developed in unprecedented numbers; 90 per cent of the prescriptions written today are for drugs that did not exist 20 years ago. Unfortunately, many of the new drugs have had unexpected and often dangerous side effects. Public Health officials estimate that about 1.3 million Americans each year are incapacitated for a day or more, or require medical attention, because of side reactions to drugs.

While drugs must meet Government safety standards, not even the most extensive laboratory tests required today can reveal all the possible effects of a drug under all conditions, or over a long period. Thalidomide, which was tested and cleared for use in several European countries, was considered one of the least toxic sedatives ever developed—until thousands of deformed babies—many of them without arms and legs—were born to women who had taken the drug during pregnancy. Sometimes the effects of a drug are far more subtle. Millions of people had used the tetracyclines, broad-spectrum antibiotics, over a period of 15 years before it was found that when the drugs are taken by expectant mothers, they lodge in the bone tissue, nails and teeth of the unborn babies, possibly interfering with the development of their bones and teeth.

Adverse reactions to drugs often take the form of allergies. Penicillin in particular causes allergic reactions ranging from skin rashes to death in some 5 to 10 per cent of the population. Since the chances of an allergic reaction increase with every dose of the drug, the number of persons sensitized to it increases annually. As a precaution, physicians are now using penicillin with greater restraint than when it was first put into general use after World War II.

The need for new tests

Modern man comes into daily contact with large numbers of chemicals. Each year modern technology produces some 500 new industrial and pharmaceutical compounds which rapidly spread throughout the nation and whose cumulative, delayed effects are unknown. To preserve health in the midst of this flood of chemicals requires a fine sense of balance. All these products are intended to bring some kind of benefit, and standard tests usually ensure that they have no immediate toxic effect. Yet it is clear that more sophisticated tests which take into account long-term effects must be developed and used routinely before any new chemical is released to the public—that a new science of "prospective" toxicology needs developing.

If authoritative, long-range forecasts are made early enough, both industry and the public willingly accept them for their own safety, as was shown when early research sounded the first warnings concerning atomic energy. In the 1950s, long before atomic energy was widely used for industrial purposes, the National Academy of Sciences began to study the effects of radiation on human beings. At the same time, comparable scientific bodies in Europe launched similar studies. For the first time in the history of civilization, scientific organizations, with government endorsement, were investigating the dangers that lay in a new technology before the technology was fully developed. In the U.S., the Academy's

RADIOACTIVE LICHEN *(above)* is the first step in a chain that causes high accumulations of radioactivity in the bodies of people in northern latitudes. The lichen, a staple food of reindeer, has been collecting radioactive dust from atomic fallout over a period of years. The flesh of the reindeer in turn is eaten by the Lapps and other northerners *(below)*. By 1964, body radioactivity among some Lapps had risen above safety levels established by the U.S. Federal Radiation Council.

reports, issued over a period of years, led to the establishment of basic safeguards in the construction of atomic-power plants and in the use of radioactive tracers. The Academy's early finding that all ionizing radiation damages living cells to some extent resulted in the removal of fluoroscopes from shoe stores and in a drastic reduction of routine fluoroscopic examinations for children. Obstetricians limited the X-raying of pregnant women, and physicians and dentists everywhere began to use X-rays with greater caution. The Academy is still continuing its studies of the effects of radiation on all aspects of human health. As part of this program it is studying the disposal of radioactive wastes—a good example of a problem in prospective toxicology that may possibly be solved before it becomes acute.

By the exercise of this kind of foresight, a booming economy that depends on a constant flow of new products need not conflict with the claims of human health. No one wants to turn the clock back to a world without automobiles, pesticides and antibiotics. It should be possible instead to determine the hazards involved in each, weigh them against the benefits, and control these man-made marvels accordingly. As man creates still more dangerous products in the future, it will become more and more essential for him to scrutinize their risks beforehand, so that he can make well-informed judgments about their use.

The Pollutions of a City

Urban, industrialized civilization is increasingly choking on its own wastes. Nowhere is the pollution problem more apparent than in the largest U.S. city, New York. Every day its sewers pour out a half billion gallons of raw filth—enough to spread a carpet one foot deep over a two-lane highway stretching from Manhattan to Norfolk, Virginia. Every month its chimneys spew out more than 20,000 tons of soot and 40,000 tons of sulfur dioxide. Pollution's toll in human health is only surmised, though studies are under way. But the damage to property is known: nationwide it comes to between seven and 11 billion dollars a year. The problems New York faces are unique only in their magnitude. Nationally, the production of waste is so great and so damaging to air and water that Harvard professor Gordon M. Fair has observed that "the conquest of outer space might eventually become a necessity for survival rather than a pawn for prestige."

A SOOTY MANHATTAN BLOSSOM
Soot from the city's smokestacks speckles a planting of chrysanthemums in New York's Central Park. The soot, while unsightly, is nowhere near so injurious as the invisible poisons the plant may have absorbed from the polluted air. An analysis of its tissues might reveal the presence of such substances as hydrogen fluoride, chlorine, acrolein, sulfur dioxide and ammonia.

Safe Harbor for Sewage

In 1524 explorer Giovanni da Verrazano found New York harbor waters "beautiful." Recently a pollution expert described the area around the Statue of Liberty as "a cesspool." Two mistakes helped muddy New York's waters. Operating at first on the adage that "dilution is the solution to pollution," New York City used its harbor as a sewer. By 1915, 540 of its 570 miles of waterfront were considered unfit for bathing. Since then, the city has spent $500 million on sewage treatment plants —but it has also made its second serious error. To save money, the pipes to the new plants were made to double as storm drains. But even light rains inundated the plants, forcing them to release raw sewage. Replacing the combined sewers would have cost a prohibitive $2.5 billion. Result: New York now spends up to $100 million a year on building treatment plants—but its waters are even more polluted than a half century ago.

UNFILTERED FILTH
Untreated sewage pours from a pipe directly into New York harbor. Despite the hundreds of millions the city has spent on sewage abatement, one half of its billion-gallon daily output still goes untreated. Across the nation, there are some 2,000 other cities, with an aggregate population of 15 million, that similarly dump their raw sewage directly into nearby waters.

STATEN ISLAND BEACH SCENE
A mass of junk-strewn ooze befouls a Staten Island beach before moving sluggishly seaward. Annually, public-health authorities warn the people not to bathe at one of the borough's beaches—after which the Parks Department opens the beach and staffs it with lifeguards.

PERSISTENT FACTORY POLLUTANTS
Industrial wastes from factories that line New Jersey's Hackensack River flow into Upper New York Bay. Although industrial waste does not breed bacteria, its chemicals may be poisonous if pumped into fresh water used for drinking.

Confusion on Pollution

When is a harbor too polluted? Water unsafe to swim in may be safe to fish in; and water so dirty it suffocates fish is still navigable. Complicating the problem of getting agreement—and action—on pollution is a matter of jurisdiction. Pollution is often an interstate problem. Involved in New York harbor are scores of governmental bodies: the Interstate Sanitation Commission, the Coast Guard, U.S. Army Corps of Engineers, the Department of Health, Education and Welfare, and the states of New York and New Jersey, along with health departments in dozens of cities. On one occasion New Jersey closed part of the harbor to clam harvesting; a federal agency then said pollution was so bad there that it was launching an investigation—and an interstate commission thereupon confused everyone by declaring the waters were actually "in very good condition."

A STAIN ON THE WATER
In order to study the distribution of wastes, heavily polluted water emptying into New York harbor is stained pink by federal researchers, using rhodamine B, a dye for coloring lipstick.

POLLUTION'S PROGRESS
Thirty minutes after the dye drop, the river is raspberry red, and the investigators' boat follows the dye's progress. It is often difficult to ascertain the concentration of pollution and its rate of dissipation under the in-and-out influence of tidal water movements. Because of this back-and-forth motion, sewage from New York City may take 16 days to reach the sea.

MAPPING THE POLLUTED AREAS
This map of Greater New York shows that almost the entire shoreline is polluted to some degree. The darker the area, the heavier the concentration. Coney Island's famous beach is constantly threatened, but future plans call hopefully for an increase in usable beaches.

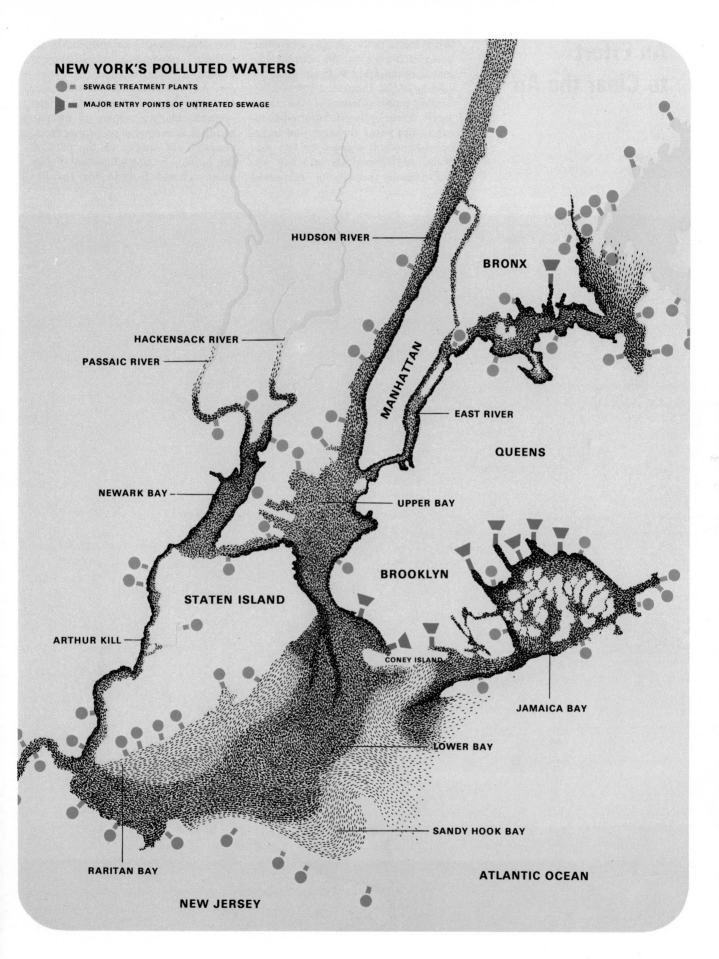

NEW YORK'S POLLUTED WATERS

● ▬ SEWAGE TREATMENT PLANTS

▼ ▬ MAJOR ENTRY POINTS OF UNTREATED SEWAGE

HUDSON RIVER

BRONX

HACKENSACK RIVER

PASSAIC RIVER

MANHATTAN

EAST RIVER

QUEENS

NEWARK BAY

UPPER BAY

BROOKLYN

STATEN ISLAND

ARTHUR KILL

CONEY ISLAND

JAMAICA BAY

LOWER BAY

RARITAN BAY

SANDY HOOK BAY

ATLANTIC OCEAN

NEW JERSEY

111

An Effort
to Clear the Air

While water pollution was a problem recognized even by the ancient Romans, air pollution was rare until the coming of the Industrial Revolution. Today, power plants by the thousands, factories by the hundred-thousands and home furnaces and internal-combustion engines by the millions expel chemicals into the air.

Physicians have long suspected that contaminated air contributes to asthma, pneumonia, tuberculosis, bronchitis, emphysema and lung cancer. Air containing pollutants that eat away steel and building stone seems so likely a menace to human health that in spite of resistance from industry and apathy on the part of the public, halting steps are being taken on a wide front to clear the air.

A PALL OF POLLUTION

Smoke from factory chimneys in New Jersey is swept across the Hudson to New York City by prevailing westerly winds. Only a few New Jersey industries have taken remedial steps. Though complaints pour in, municipalities seldom take action for fear of driving industry off.

THE HOME FIRES BURN

Thick smoke belches from apartment houses burning No. 6 oil, New York's most common heating fuel, of which 1.5 billion gallons are burned annually. This fuel, with a 3 per cent sulfur content, is a major source of sulfur dioxide in the air. Soft coal, another source of pollution, is burned by the public utilities; they account for 60 per cent of summertime pollution.

TROUBLE FROM TAIL PIPES

Exhaust from one of New York's 1.5 million autos expels a variety of air pollutants, including acrolein, an eye irritant, benzpyrene, a cancer agent, plus oxides of nitrogen which irritate the lungs. Auto fumes constitute 30 per cent of the pollutants in the city's air. Devices which eliminate some of the noxious gases did not become mandatory on new cars until 1963.

THE POLLUTANT CALLED "PAN"
Silvery damage caused by polluted air mars the underside of this beet leaf grown near New York. Plant pathologists at Rutgers University believe the responsible agent is a chemical called "Pan"—actually peroxyacylnitrate. A poisonous gas, Pan is produced, along with other pollutants, when hydrocarbons are burned. The leaf damage is caused by Pan's oxidizing action.

The Toll of Topsy-turvy Air

Air pollution at its worst occurs during a meteorological mix-up called inversion. At such times the air over a region is trapped; when the area is urban or industrialized, pollutants are not blown away on the winds, but build up in the air, sometimes to dangerous levels (below).

The pollutants thus trapped include acids known to be harmful to building materials and to plants (opposite). Since the 1950s the U.S. Government and such institutions as the Cornell University Medical College have been conducting studies to determine if a similar and direct correlation exists between air pollution and human disease. Researchers have not proved a direct laboratory relationship, but are sure one exists.

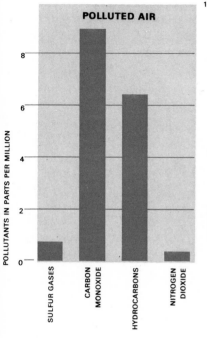

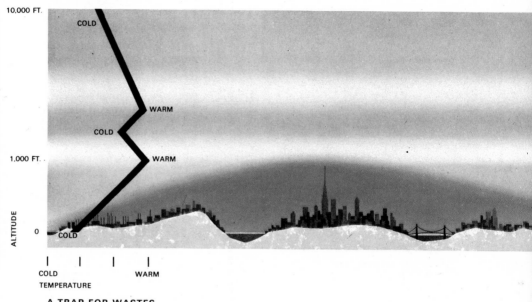

A TRAP FOR WASTES

From time to time, an air inversion creates a huge dome of stagnant air (tinted olive) over New York City. The normal temperature is inverted; instead of warm air (light tone) rising and dispersing, cool ground air is trapped by a layer of warm air above it. As the inversion continues, air pollutants pile up—as the chart at left, showing a typical bad day in 1962, indicates.

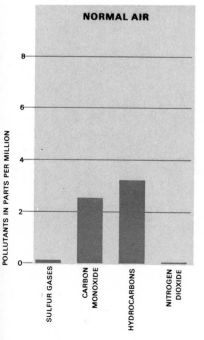

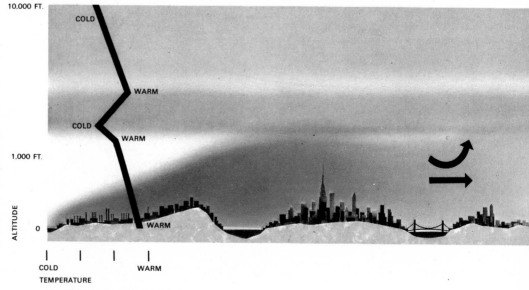

BLOWING AWAY THE POISONS

Early-morning air inversions are fairly common in the city. However, by midmorning the sun heats the ground-level air, and it rises. Cool air rushes to replace the departed air, and breezes (arrows) help disperse the pollutants, leaving a more or less normal day (chart at left). Such ordinary ground-level inversions (bottom layers) may occur 20 times a month in autumn.

Pollution at the Precipice

In the 1930s soil erosion was considered one of the most important threats to the nation's natural resources. In the years since that time its place has been taken to a great extent by air- and water-pollution. Some officials are trying to cope with the menace. Improved facilities for sewage *(opposite)*, detergents that microbes can break down, tighter pollution-control laws and an aroused public opinion may yet prevent the U.S. from choking on its own wastes.

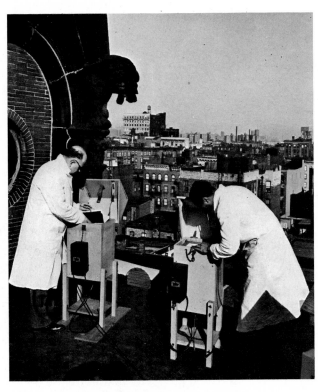

ANALYZING THE AIR
Technicians check air-sampling equipment on top of the New York Department of Air Pollution Control laboratory. The Department's 36 inspectors roam the city looking for everything from smoky chimneys to people burning leaves. About 1,000 summonses a year are issued.

A TANK FOR SEWAGE
Reinforcing rods protrude from the $160-million Newtown Creek Sewage Treatment project. Newtown, with a capacity of 300 million gallons a day and serving 2.5 million people in Brooklyn, Manhattan and Queens, was designed to be the city's biggest sewage plant.

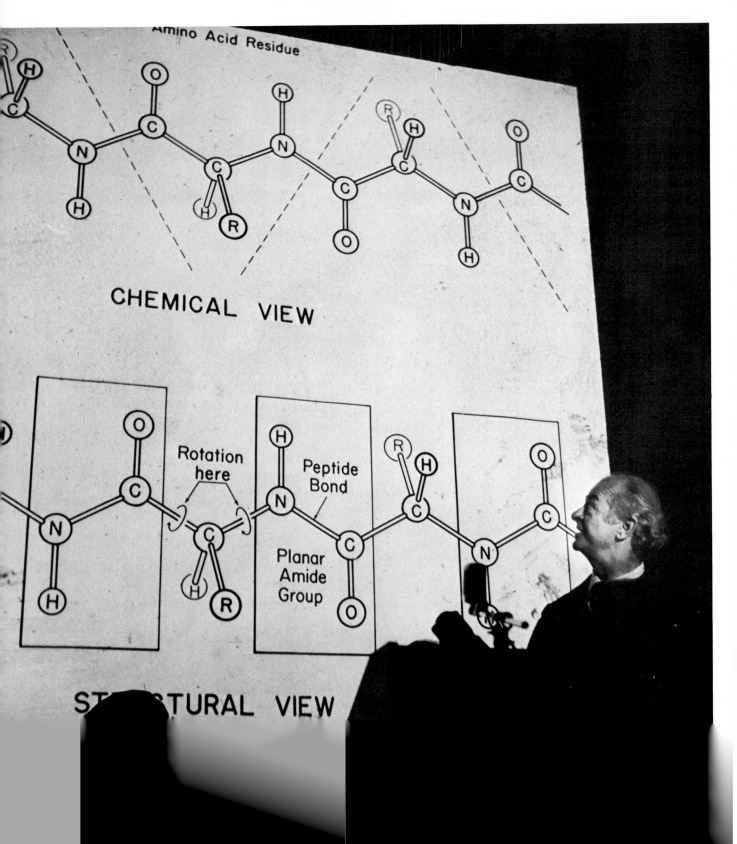

SOME OF THE ILLNESSES that afflict man have their origins in the physical equipment he inherited from his parents—in the unique set of genes with which he was born. Exactly how many disorders are thus inescapably built into human beings not even the modern geneticist knows for sure. Both heredity and environment are involved to some extent in all disease. In some cases, environmental factors obviously play the critical role: a sufficiently large dose of barbiturates will kill anyone, regardless of his physical inheritance. But geneticists now know that each person's success in fighting off infections and other threats to health depends partly on his individual genetic endowment. Furthermore, many rare and strange diseases are definitely inherited.

The genes' role in the body's adaptation to the environment is illustrated by the reactions of different types of people to sunlight. Those with fair skin must take care not to be badly burned by a day at the beach. Darker-skinned people—who have inherited a better capacity to produce the pigment involved in tanning—adapt to sunlight with less skin damage. As one consequence, people with fair skins are more likely than brunets to develop skin cancer. Thus, although the cancer itself may not be inherited, certain people may be more vulnerable to it because of their genes.

Genes are probably the most intricate bundles of information known. They determine the nature of every cell in every living organism, establishing its species, sex and the general pattern of its individual characteristics. Humans, who are composed of trillions of highly specialized cells, have many thousands of genes. They are gathered in 46 curiously shaped agglomerations of matter called chromosomes, which come in pairs—one member of each pair from each parent. This basic genetic material accomplishes its many tasks by duplicating itself completely in every new cell grown by the body; from headquarters in the cell nucleus it then directs the cell's development.

Genes and environment are so intertwined in their effects upon development that a geneticist's hardest task is often to unravel what is genetic and what is not. A baby with a perfectly sound genetic inheritance, for example, may be born with a congenital defect—that is, a defect present at birth—because he was damaged by his environment. This damage may have been caused by anything from a virus in his mother's bloodstream to an injury during delivery. Even certain diseases that seemed to run in families have turned out to be caused by environment. It had been known for a long time, for instance, that a large percentage of the females of certain strains of mice developed mammary cancer. The disease seemed definitely hereditary—until it was discovered that the milk of mice from these particular strains contained a cancer-inducing virus. By letting newborn mice of these strains suckle on mice

THE IMPORTANCE OF PROTEINS
Dr. Linus Pauling, whose early investigations into the bonding of molecules won him the Nobel Prize in 1954, here illustrates a lecture on genetic defects with a diagram of a protein molecule. By proving that a defective protein causes sickle-cell anemia, he helped to demonstrate that inherited diseases may be caused by faulty body chemistry at the molecular level.

119

of another strain, experimenters succeeded in ending this apparently hereditary trait.

Even when a disease is genetic, the geneticist may find it impossible to predict which apparently normal member of a family will develop it. One genetic disease, Huntington's chorea, may not show its first symptoms—involuntary jerking movements of the body and limbs—until the victim is past middle age and has children. Only then does he discover that he is doomed to a progressive degeneration of the nervous system ending in death. Moreover, the statistical chances are that half his children will die the same dreadful death; since there is no way to tell which children will be afflicted, they must wait in terrible suspense for the rest of their lives, for the disease may strike at any age.

A late-blooming science

Genetics is still looking for many answers, for it has acquired most of its body of knowledge only in the last few decades. It got off to a late start in 1900, some 40 years after its foundations had been meticulously laid by the Austrian botanist and monk, Gregor Johann Mendel. Mendel's hobby was crossbreeding plants, and he set out to determine whether the characteristics of hybrids could be predicted, or whether —as botanists and gardeners of the time assumed—they were a matter of blind chance. Beginning in the 1840s, in a monastery garden at Brünn, he raised several carefully selected varieties of garden peas for many generations, cross-fertilizing them again and again, and carefully noting the results. In 1865 he read a paper to the Brünn Society for the Study of Natural Science, in which he described the exact frequency with which certain hereditary traits could be expected to turn up—with variations due to chance—in successive generations. He had reduced the mysteries of cultivating hybrids to a few dazzlingly simple statistical laws—in other words, to a science of genetics.

Mendel's paper caused scarcely a ripple. Not even the leading botanists of the time, to whom he hopefully sent copies, grasped its significance. Mendel's work went virtually unnoticed until 1900, when three botanists in three different countries, working independently, suddenly rediscovered it within a period of four months. Soon thereafter, a fourth botanist, the British William Bateson, became fascinated with the possibility that the Mendelian laws of inherited characteristics might apply to men as well as plants. In 1905 he coined the word "genetics" in a letter proposing that the University of Cambridge found an institute for the study of heredity. The university rejected the proposal, but Bateson continued his attempts to arouse medical interest in human genetics.

His enthusiasm infected at least one physician, his friend Archibald Garrod, whose interests were largely biochemical. Garrod was making

THE FIRST MENDELIAN LAW of heredity states that inherited traits are "segregated" —i.e., they can emerge in pure form even after several generations of crossing with other traits. If a pure-colored snapdragon and a white one are crossed, as shown, the first generation will be of an intermediate shade, but when two hybrid intermediates are crossed, the inherited original colors reappear separately in half the offspring: one pure-colored flower and one pure white for every two intermediates. The intermediate descendants will produce pure offspring in the same proportion. The pure plants produce only their own color. Like color traits, some genetic diseases can re-emerge in families after several generations.

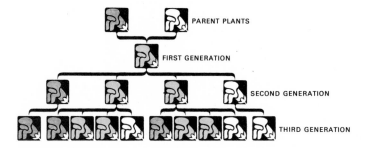

PARENT PLANTS

FIRST GENERATION

SECOND GENERATION

THIRD GENERATION

an intensive study of a number of rare diseases—among them alkapto-
nuria, a condition characterized by the excretion of black urine—and
he eventually established to his own satisfaction that they were not only
caused by faults in the body chemistry, but were inherited as well. Bateson acted as publicist for Garrod's work, lecturing neurologists on the
possibility of inherited disease, and in 1908 Garrod himself gave a series
of lectures before the Royal College of Physicians, summarizing them
under the title "Inborn Errors of Metabolism."

Biochemical genetics was born with these lectures. Garrod was decades ahead of his time, but geneticists have since confirmed that all
inheritance is a matter of passing along chemical instructions. In 1933
the American geneticist Thomas Hunt Morgan won a Nobel Prize for
establishing that chromosomes were the material of heredity. The name
"genes," which had been in use for years, was quickly applied to the
presumed units of chromosomal matter, on the supposition that each
unit was a determinant of some hereditary trait. Geneticists today work
with molecular units, but the term "genes" is still in use.

A poisonous inheritance

A classic example of an inherited biochemical disease is phenylketonuria (PKU), a condition in which a single vital enzyme normally manufactured by the liver is missing. In 1934 a Norwegian physician-biochem-
ist, Asbjørn Følling, responded to a mother's plea that he try to help
her two severely retarded children. For years she had gone from one
doctor to the next in fruitless attempts to find out the cause of their
condition. Among other signs of the disease was a peculiar musty odor.

Dr. Følling examined her children in minute detail. Among other
things, he tested their urine with ferric chloride, which changes color
in the presence of certain foreign substances. He was surprised to see
the specimens turn blue-green, a color he had never encountered in such
testing. Intrigued, he spent three months isolating the substance responsible for this chemical reaction, finally identifying it as a by-product of
phenylalanine, an amino acid present in proteins. A second by-product
of phenylalanine was present in the children's sweat and accounted for
their strange odor.

Tests of children in nearby institutions for the retarded revealed
many more patients with the same symptoms, incuding two brother-
sister pairs. Dr. Følling then hypothesized that the abnormality was an
inherited error of metabolism—that normally harmless phenylalanine,
consumed by these children in milk, meat and other proteins, was turning into a toxic substance instead of being properly metabolized.

In the years since, researchers have confirmed Dr. Følling's hypoth-
esis and have figured out the metabolic error involved—a lack of one liver

enzyme that metabolizes phenylalanine. About one person in every 70 carries one faulty gene for the manufacture of this enzyme, but in these cases another, normal gene can still perform the function, and the person is spared PKU. Trouble arises only when two PKU carriers produce an offspring who inherits the wrong gene from both of them—an event which happens only once in every 10,000 to 20,000 live births.

The baby born with a pair of PKU genes comes into the world apparently normal, since while he was in the womb his mother metabolized his food for him. But for him this is a violently hostile world. With his first food, milk—including his mother's milk—he takes in phenylalanine. Since he cannot metabolize it, it rapidly builds up in his blood to levels about 20 times above normal, turning into a poison. After a few weeks, by-products of the acid show up in the urine. If left untreated, the child shows definite deterioration within a few months. His brain is irreversibly damaged, and by two or three years of age he has sunk to an I.Q. well below 50, and often close to 20, compared to the average 100. Half of all PKU victims die before the age of 20.

A diet to save the brain

About 8,000 such unfortunates were still alive in the U.S. as of the 1960s, but the number was expected to decline. For although medicine cannot yet provide PKU victims with their missing enzyme, it has learned to manipulate their environment in such a way that phenylalanine never accumulates in dangerous quantities during the crucial years of brain growth. Several synthetic foods with safe levels of phenylalanine have been developed, and when given early enough in life they greatly benefit the majority of phenylketonurics. At first the children were launched on such a diet as soon as evidence of PKU showed up in their urine—about a month after birth—but in 1961 a simple blood test developed by Dr. Robert Guthrie made it possible to detect the genetic defect in most cases during the first few days of life. In 1963 Massachusetts became the first state to make the test mandatory in all hospitals, soon after a sampling of 84,000 newborns turned up 10 cases of PKU—twice the expected number. Those 10 and the others who have been found since will now have a chance to develop normally. It may be possible to modify their special diet at the age of five or six, when the fully developed brain seems more resistant to damage from toxic levels of phenylalanine.

Phenylketonuria is rare, but the sum of all the diseases that can be inherited from healthy parents creates a grave burden for mankind. Although the most severely injurious genes tend to be eliminated from the population by the process of natural selection, many others survive. Furthermore, genes sometimes change, or mutate—almost always with an unfavorable effect. Increased exposure to radiation in modern times may

AN ABNORMAL ARRANGEMENT of chromosomes, though rare, sometimes occurs in humans, invariably causing grave congenital defects. Diagramed below are the chromosomes characteristic of one kind of Mongoloid idiot: instead of the normal 23 pairs of chromosomes, the 21st cluster is composed of three chromosomes (the last pair are the normal sex chromosomes of a male). The mistake is believed to be the result of a faulty division of one of the parent's sex cells shortly before conception. Most Mongoloids die young, but if they survive and have children, there is a 50 per cent chance their children will inherit the disease.

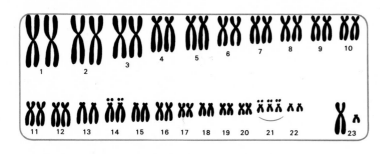

have stepped up the rate of mutations. Thus there is at all times an abundance of injurious genes in circulation. Some geneticists estimate that the number among humans probably averages four or five per person. They remain unnoticed as long as they are matched by normal genes from one parent. By the laws of chance, however, certain people carry far above average numbers of potentially harmful genes, and in the lottery of mating, faulty genes are bound to pair up fairly frequently, producing a wide range of abnormalities.

Lincoln and the Marfan syndrome

Not all such abnormalities are as devastating in their effects as PKU, by any means. The victim may remain well within the range of normal, and may go through life quite unaware that his defects are hereditary. Although neither he nor anybody else knew it in his day, for instance, Abraham Lincoln probably had a hereditary disease of the connective tissue. His unusual appearance, certain physical defects he is known to have had, and the early death of one of his children all suggest that he had the Marfan syndrome. This is a disease named after the doctor who first described it in 1896—more than 30 years after Lincoln's death. The suspicion that the Civil War President suffered from the syndrome first occurred to Dr. Harold Schwartz, a California physician, in 1959, when he recognized the disorder in a boy of seven, and learned that the youngster shared an ancestor with Lincoln. The boy, like Lincoln, was exceptionally long-limbed—one sign of the disease. Combing through historical records, Dr. Schwartz concluded that Lincoln may have inherited the Marfan syndrome from his father's side of the family.

Besides an elongated skeleton, the Marfan syndrome involves numerous asymmetries in the body and often includes eye trouble and cardiac disease. Lincoln's hands, arms and legs were not only unusually long; the right and left sides were strikingly disproportionate. Casts made in the year of his nomination show that his left hand was much longer than his right hand, with the left middle finger particularly elongated. Yet his left thumb was nearly half an inch shorter than his right thumb. Because of slight irregularities in his facial structure, Lincoln had difficulty coordinating his eyes. He also suffered from severe farsightedness. Of all the parts of his body, the longest and thinnest were probably his legs, which a contemporary described as "spiderlike." When Lincoln was seated, he did not seem taller than anyone else, but his knees rose well above the plane of his thighs, and as his law partner William H. Herndon observed, "it was only when he stood up that he loomed above other men."

Lincoln's father had been blind in one eye, with poor vision in the other. Lincoln's son Robert also had considerable difficulty with his eyes. Another son, Tad, suffered from a speech defect and misshapen palate, and died at 18 after probable cardiac difficulty. Two other sons and a grandchild may have had similar complications.

An old trait, suddenly lethal

Changes in environment brought about by the advance of civilization are turning up genetic peculiarities that were once so inconsequential they went unnoticed, but that now have become suddenly dangerous. For example, thousands of Afrikaners—all descendants of one Dutch immigrant who settled in South Africa in the 17th Century—share a hereditary trait which makes barbiturates and some other drugs mortally dangerous for them. Until the 20th Century, the only sign of the metabolic anomaly for most of these people was a sensitive skin that abraded easily, producing frequent sores on their hands—a mild disorder called porphyria variegata. As modern medicines began to be introduced, however, many Afrikaners fell acutely ill, suffering delusions and complaining of pains for which no cause could be found. In many cases, the illness became progressively worse, ending in paralysis and death. A young English doctor practicing in South Africa, Geoffrey Dean, was one of the first to notice that all the victims had become ill after being treated with barbiturates or sulfonamides.

As Dr. Dean pieced the case histories together, it became evident that almost every step physicians had taken to alleviate the illness had made it worse. When the first exposure to barbiturates produced abdominal pain, many victims were given sedatives containing more barbiturates. These, in turn, would aggravate the pain so violently that in many cases surgeons felt compelled to operate immediately. During this surgery the patient might be anesthetized with Pentothal—one of the worst forms of poison for a porphyric—followed, once again, by heavy doses of sedatives that would spell his death. One South African doctor precipitated his own attack of porphyria by taking sulfonamide tablets to treat a sinus infection. He developed pains and delusions of persecution, was hospitalized for two months, lost 120 pounds, and did not fully recover for a year. After the cause of the disease became known, Dr. Dean wrote a letter to a woman related to known porphyrics, warning her not to take any barbiturates. The letter arrived too late; the woman had been given her first barbiturates just a few days before, and was already ill. Soon after the letter came, she died.

A number of other genetic anomalies cause their sufferers to react to certain substances as violently as porphyrics do to drugs. Most of these anomalies were originally associated with populations from a particular region. One of them, a long-mysterious disease called favism, may kill its victims if they so much as walk through a field of fava beans—a broad bean widely consumed in the Mediterranean countries. Something in the

LINCOLN'S LONG LEGS, evident in this drawing from a contemporary photograph, may have been the result of a hereditary disorder affecting connective tissue. The disease was recently identified in a boy distantly related to Lincoln. The gene causing it may have reached both victims in unbroken lines of inheritance going back at least to their nearest common ancestor, Mordecai Lincoln II, born in 1686. As the chart below shows, Lincoln was descended from Mordecai and his first wife. The contemporary boy's mother is the direct descendant of a line of Lincoln males born of Mordecai and his second wife.

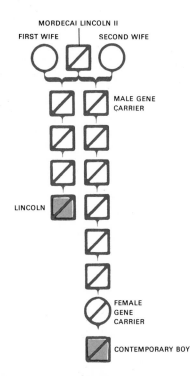

MORDECAI LINCOLN II

FIRST WIFE   SECOND WIFE

MALE GENE CARRIER

LINCOLN

FEMALE GENE CARRIER

CONTEMPORARY BOY

bean causes the sudden destruction of their red blood cells, resulting in a severe, often lethal anemia. Recent experience with primaquine—a drug used in the cure of malaria—indicates that some 10 per cent of all Negroes may have a similar reaction on taking the drug, and that large numbers of them may also react to sulfonamide and even aspirin with severe anemia. Chemical tests reveal that the anemia in all these cases is caused by the reduced activity of one enzyme in the red blood cells.

A more common hereditary anemia—called sickle-cell because of the peculiar crescent shape of its victim's red blood cells—flourishes in malarial regions, and researchers are beginning to see a link between its presence and a successful adaptation to the environment. People who inherit only one sickle-cell gene have a greater than normal resistance to malaria, but the price is paid by their brothers and sisters who may inherit two genes for sickle cells and die of severe anemia before adolescence. In some areas of Africa, 40 per cent of the population are carriers of sickle-cell genes. On the Mediterranean island of Sardinia, sickle-cell genes are prevalent among the inhabitants of the lowlands, which were formerly malarial, while the people living in the mountains have no malaria and few are afflicted with sickle-cell genes.

The disappearing sickle cells

Such cases have led researchers to the conclusion that many of the genes that cause disease originally became prevalent in certain populations in response to some environmental need—and indeed in some cases still provide protection. In regions where such genes serve no beneficial purpose, they tend to disappear. Thus in America, where there is little malaria, the incidence of sickle-cell genes among Negroes has been declining rapidly.

Many undiscovered genes with latent dangers or advantages are undoubtedly scattered throughout the general population. This is not necessarily an undesirable situation. Their existence makes it likely that at least some part of the population will be able to adapt to whatever new situations occur, thus ensuring that the species will survive. The geneticists' term for this state of affairs is "balanced polymorphism."

An example of polymorphism in the human species is its variety of inherited blood groups. Blood has been studied more intensively by geneticists than any other human tissue, probably because it is easiest to test. In 1900, when the science of genetics was just getting started, an Austrian pathologist, Karl Landsteiner, distinguished four human blood types, which are now called O, A, B and AB. Since then, scientists have found a large number of genetically determined variations in the blood. Some of these variations are exceedingly rare. In 1964 a Zulu woman in Johannesburg—one of only two known people in the world with a certain

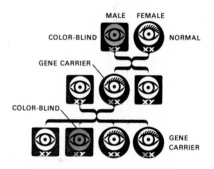

COLOR BLINDNESS is one of a number of "sex-linked" genetic disorders which are transmitted by females but usually turn up in alternate generations of males. Females have a matched pair of X-shaped sex chromosomes—one inherited from each parent —but males have an unmatched pair: one X inherited from the mother and one Y inherited from the father. Because the gene causing color blindness is in the X chromosome, color-blind men inherit the condition only from their mothers and pass the gene along only to their daughters. If a daughter's second X chromosome is normal, she will not be color-blind, but she may give the disorder to her son.

type of blood—was called upon to donate a pint of blood to save the life of an unborn baby in Philadelphia.

The significance of the many new blood factors that have been discovered recently is still unknown. The presence or absence of the Rh factor, for instance, may confer some special advantages, but geneticists remain in the dark as to what they might be. The Rh factor, discovered in 1940, is a substance found in the blood of rhesus monkeys and in most—but not all—humans. The disadvantages of this uneven distribution have turned out to be acute. When a woman whose blood has no Rh factor bears a succession of children with Rh positive blood inherited from the father, her blood may become sensitized to the foreign factor, and she manufactures antibodies that enter the infant's bloodstream and destroy his blood cells. The firstborn almost always escapes harm, but subsequent babies may suffer brain damage, or they may be stillborn or afflicted with a deadly jaundice, with the chances of damage increasing with every birth.

A complete change of blood

Fortunately, medicine has learned how to help such infants by changing their internal environment to one less hostile to their genetic endowment. Tests can determine whether or not a mother is sensitized to her baby's blood type, and whether the baby's blood is being damaged. In case of damage, he is given massive transfusions of the mother's blood type—which his mother's antibodies will not destroy. The earlier his blood is replaced with his mother's type, the better chance he has of developing normally. The procedure is usually done the moment he is born, but techniques have recently been developed for providing him with transfusions while still in the womb.

So far medical genetics has thrown the most light on those relatively rare diseases—like phenylketonuria, porphyria and sickle-cell anemia—which involve clear-cut chemical disorders caused by a single gene, and whose transmission in families can be traced with relative ease. It has been a far more frustrating problem for geneticists to get at the root of the many common afflictions which they suspect are partially genetic, but which do not include easily identified chemical processes—because an unknown number of genes may be interacting with many complex environmental factors.

Few geneticists doubt that such widespread illnesses as diabetes, rheumatoid arthritis and even schizophrenia have genetic components. Yet these illnesses seem to be precipitated by environmental factors, and the part played by genes is hard to prove. At best, geneticists must rely on guilt by association—on showing that disease X is more common within certain families than in the population at large, or that identical

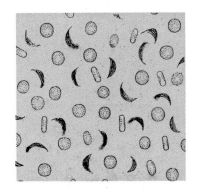

SICKLE-CELL ANEMIA is one of a few genetic disorders whose exact chemistry is known: because of a single variation in the intricate chemical structure of hemoglobin, red blood cells assume a crescent shape *(black, above)* when their oxygen supply is reduced. These sickle cells are destroyed by the body, and the result is anemia. Those who inherit one gene for the disorder may have mild anemia, but those who inherit two, one from each parent, have almost nothing but sickle cells, and cannot survive beyond adolescence without extensive medical care.

twins (who are born with identical genes) both suffer from it much more frequently than do pairs of nonidentical twins.

Nevertheless it is far from certain that even identical twins will both have such a disease. For example, despite the fact that diabetes runs in families, if one identical twin has the disease, there is only a 62-per cent chance that his twin will have it too. Evidently variations in environment, particularly in diet, account for considerable divergence in this "concordance," as it is called. It is far less likely that nonidentical twins will both suffer from diabetes; it has turned up in only 12 per cent of the cases studied.

Diabetes, far more widespread than is generally realized, affects about 3.4 million Americans. About two million know they have the disease; the rest are unaware that they are affected. The incidence and mortality of diabetes are highest in affluent nations, for the disease seems to be related to rich diets. A large number of diabetics develop the disease during middle age, after a period of being overweight. The incidence of the disease dropped sharply during both World Wars, wherever serious food shortages developed.

The basic cause of the ailment remains unknown. Its immediate cause is a deficiency of working insulin in the blood. Some diabetics are believed to need greater amounts of insulin than they produce; still others may produce insulin in adequate amounts, but it somehow becomes inactivated by the body. The result in either case is a deficit in a substance essential to the metabolism of sugar, leading to the constant excretion of unmetabolized sugar in large volumes of urine. Lost with the sugar are many salts and minerals essential to the maintenance of health. At the same time, the body burns excessive amounts of fat in its need for energy, and by-products of this fat accumulate in the blood in toxic quantities. The whole process was well described in a Second Century definition of diabetes by a Roman physician: "A melting down of the flesh and the limbs to urine."

Modern control of an ancient malady

The course of diabetes, which once commonly ended in diabetic coma and death, has been greatly modified since the 1920s, when it was discovered that victims were helped by injections of insulin extracted from the pancreases of animals. By limiting their intake of sugar and taking insulin injections or the newer, oral antidiabetic drugs, most diabetics can function quite normally. Many who would once have died in childhood now survive and bear children of their own. As a result, if the disease is genetic, it must be assumed that the number of diabetics will increase in the population. "One may speculate," a leading geneticist, Theodosius Dobzhansky, has written, "that . . . persons with diabetic genotypes [i.e., genetic endowments] could be reasonably well off in an environment where factories maintained a regular supply of synthetic insulin. Diabetes would then be an environmental disease caused by insulin deficiency, like the once dreaded but now fortunately preventable scurvy, which is caused by a deficiency of vitamin C."

The tangled causes of schizophrenia

Environment and heredity are even more difficult to disentangle in mental illness. Schizophrenia, which fills more than a quarter of all U.S. hospital beds, continues to defy explanation. While a good deal of evidence points to a genetic predisposition—at least for some forms of schizophrenia—early childhood experiences and emotional stress are also factors in its occurrence.

Researchers have found measurable metabolic abnormalities in schizophrenic patients, suggesting that the disease has a biochemical component. The evidence that it is genetic is far from conclusive, however. It is not clear whether the chemical abnormalities are the cause or the result of the illness. Recent experiments with monkeys have shown that isolation during infancy and inadequate rearing will also produce metabolic abnormalities, as well as schizophrenialike behavior: fear, withdrawal and inappropriate responses. On the other hand, schizophrenic concordance among identical twins ranges from 67 to 86 per cent; among nonidentical twins it is only 3 to 15 per cent.

In recent years, highly sophisticated research techniques have enabled scientists to study the genetic material in cell nuclei in terms of the giant molecules of which it is composed. They are unraveling step by step the infinitely complex mechanisms through which these molecules transmit instructions for new cell growth. Eventually they may be able to map the genetic material so precisely that they will know which molecules perform which functions, and can identify the aberrants involved in many diseases that now remain inexplicable. But even if geneticists should manage to achieve this, their success will not ensure that these aberrations could be eliminated from the human race by simple eugenics. Most scientists long ago abandoned the early dream that man could improve his breed by the mating of people with healthy bodies and desirable personality characteristics.

The eugenics movement was founded by a British scientist, Francis Galton, in 1883. Its aim was to improve mankind's genetic endowment of various traits, including character and disposition. Galton studied the families of eminent men and discovered that "out of the 286 judges, more than one in every nine of them have been either father, son, or brother to another judge, and the other high legal relationships have been even more numerous. There cannot, then, remain a doubt that the peculiar type of ability that is necessary to a judge is often transmitted by descent." The contributions of education and family connections in the making of judges in Victorian England were ignored. Galton also compared different races—without any scientific data—and declared that Anglo-Saxons were much superior to Negroes, although inferior to the early Athenians.

The eugenics movement, which spread to Europe and America, had a profound influence on popular thought. It influenced American immigration legislation and contributed to the Nazi doctrines of an Aryan "master race." The Nazis' extermination of millions of persons whom they considered unfit—the lame, the blind, the mentally defective as well as Jews, Gypsies and political opponents—provoked such a postwar wave of revulsion that not only eugenics but also the science of human genetics fell into disrepute.

The fact is, according to most modern geneticists, that there is simply not enough scientific information at present on which to base any recommendations for large-scale eugenic planning. Only a few geneticists, notably Herman J. Muller and Julian Huxley, have promoted radical plans for improving man by the calculated selection of parents. Dr. Muller would like to preserve semen from "outstanding" donors—the present-day counterparts of Leonardo da Vinci, Descartes, Lincoln, Pasteur and Einstein—in deep freeze and encourage couples to use it for artificial insemination.

Problems of planning a superrace

Muller's mention of Lincoln illustrates the trouble with his plan. Lincoln's four sons may have inherited his Marfan syndrome: one died young, and none led a really outstanding life. Furthermore, the late geneticist J.B.S. Haldane showed that sterilization of the unfit would have very little influence on the proportion of harmful genes scattered throughout the population; by the same token, the multiplication of "outstanding" genes, fewer in number, could have even less effect on the population at large. Finally, even if the practice of eugenics were practical and effective, the qualities considered outstanding now may not be the qualities needed in the future for survival.

There are at least two ways, however, in which to exercise helpful control over genetics and minimize the risk of genetic disease. The first is to reduce human exposure to such forces as radiation, which promote genetic mutations that are nearly always harmful. The second is to make premarital biochemical tests routine, to determine whether a prospective couple might both hand on to their children a single gene causing hereditary disease. In Italy, for instance, it has become common practice to screen schoolchildren for evidence of the gene for thalassemia,

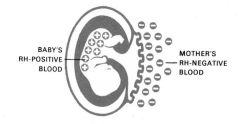

RH INCOMPATIBILITY occurs when a mother's blood is incompatible with her child's because one of them contains the protein factor known as Rh and the other does not. Incompatibility is a problem only when the fetus has Rh-positive blood, as shown here.

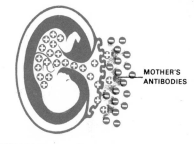

A CONFLICT comes when a baby's Rh-positive blood filters through the placenta into the mother's Rh-negative bloodstream; the mother's blood reacts by creating antibodies. She may have one Rh-positive baby safely, but the next will have trouble.

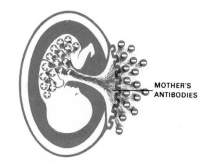

DANGER THREATENS when antibodies flow back into the baby's bloodstream, destroying his red blood cells. In up to 10 per cent of pregnancies involving Rh incompatibility, enough antibodies reach the baby to cause severe, perhaps fatal, anemia.

a severe form of anemia particularly prevalent around the Mediterranean. The children who do carry it are then warned of the dangers of future marriage with another carrier. Similar tests can detect carriers of sickle-cell anemia, phenylketonuria and other diseases. Many geneticists would like to see them used as widely as premarital tests for the Rh factor or syphilis. Even if the premarital advice is disregarded, tests would at least make possible early detection of illness in the offspring.

Apart from these measures, the genetic material packed into every cell nucleus is so complicated that it would be foolish to hope that humans can mate in such a way as to prevent all genetic disease or control all their children's characteristics.

One hopeful possibility remains for the future control of man's genetic endowment: recent experiments indicate that as much as 80 per cent of the genetic material stays inactive in the cells of higher organisms. Geneticists have just begun to learn how the genes exert their control, but the search is already on for what controls the controllers. Some genes seem to be activated by hormones, others by a change of diet. "As we learn how gene activity is controlled," biochemist A. E. Mirsky of The Rockefeller University has said, "we shall be in a position to guide it deliberately under optimal conditions." In other words, geneticists may help man make the best of the genes he has.

Living with Inherited Flaws

New medical knowledge does more than provide cures and treatment; it often helps abolish attitudes that add to the burden of disease. For five million people who inherited the mysterious and incurable disorders shown on the following pages, these burdens have sometimes been almost unbearable. At one time or another muscular dystrophy, cystic fibrosis, hemophilia, diabetes and epilepsy have all been written off as hopeless. Society once left dystrophics to wait for death; and the right of epileptics to marry was restricted by law (in 16 states it still is). But scientists, who believe they are close to solving the enigma of hereditary disease, have challenged the old attitudes. To a great extent, drugs have brought diabetes and epilepsy under control. Treatment is being developed for cystic fibrosis and hemophilia. And in a new climate of hope, dystrophics such as the student opposite are urged to enjoy life to the limit of their capacities.

A CHANCE TO DEVELOP
Confined to a wheelchair, yet eager to develop his mind, a young muscular-dystrophy patient studies biology at the Institute for Muscle Disease in New York. Education for dystrophics—who were formerly regarded as mentally retarded—is a major result of the new attitude toward the disease. Intelligence testing has shown that only the body, not the mind, is crippled by dystrophy.

PROFILE OF THE DISEASE
In these two slides, which show muscle tissue magnified 400 times, the difference between healthy tissue *(top)* and dystrophic muscle is unmistakable. In the lower slide, the even striations of healthy muscle fiber have been pushed aside by blobs of colorless fat and invading connective tissue (stained blue). As the fat builds up, the muscles gradually weaken and shrivel.

IN SEARCH OF THE CAUSE
Looking for the missing or malfunctioning biochemical substance that causes muscular dystrophy, a medical researcher injects chicken eggs with a substance called selenium. Tiny quantities of such substances are known to have an effect on the biochemistry of muscle tissue.

POSTPONING THE DAMAGE
Staving off the early leg-crippling effects of muscular dystrophy, two boys at a rehabilitation center in Houston, Texas, play, study and sleep in special pivoting beds. By keeping the feet and legs at a rigid 90° angle, the beds will hopefully slow the progressive contractures of the heel tendons that are characteristic of the disease. The beds can be bought for use at home.

A Hereditary Waster of Muscle

Muscular dystrophy is not one disease, but a group of related diseases. The boys at far left, strapped into specially built beds, are victims of the commonest, most severe form.

Some types of dystrophy are passed along by healthy mothers to their sons; others are inherited in a fashion not yet fully understood. The illness strikes in the first five years of life and pursues a relentless course that may end in death within 20 years. Just how dystrophy affects muscle is a mystery, but it seems to involve the absence or malfunctioning of some unidentified substance that nourishes healthy muscle. Whatever the process, muscle tissue is replaced by globules of fat (*opposite, top*).

Little can be done to alleviate dystrophy. But sufferers no longer wait apathetically for death to come. Instead they can use both their minds and their hands; this new and active life improves their morale and eases the burden of physical deterioration.

WORK FOR HAND AND BRAIN
Muscular-dystrophy patients at New York's Institute for Muscle Disease assemble an intricate mosaic under the supervision of a therapist (*right*). The fact that they can use their hands for such precise work long after their legs are crippled enables dystrophics to build up psychological defenses against the severe emotional stresses created as the disease wears on.

A TELLTALE HAND PRINT

In the simplest of various tests for cystic fibrosis, a patient places his hand on a testing device and the perspiration on his palm reacts with chemicals. A telltale yellow color may indicate cystic fibrosis. A normal person tested in this manner would leave a colorless hand print.

BEDTIME IN A TENT

At home, a three-year-old boy with cystic fibrosis settles down for the night inside a tent which is kept filled with a medicated mist while he sleeps. He spends an average of eight hours out of the 24 in this tent or breathing from a mask. The flask at right holds the humidifying solution.

SURVIVAL IN A GAS MASK

At the Cystic Fibrosis Clinic in Houston, children breathe antibiotic mist through translucent plastic masks as they read and play in a hospital treatment room. The drugs help to combat bacterial infection; the mist dissolves the thick deposits of mucus that form in their lungs.

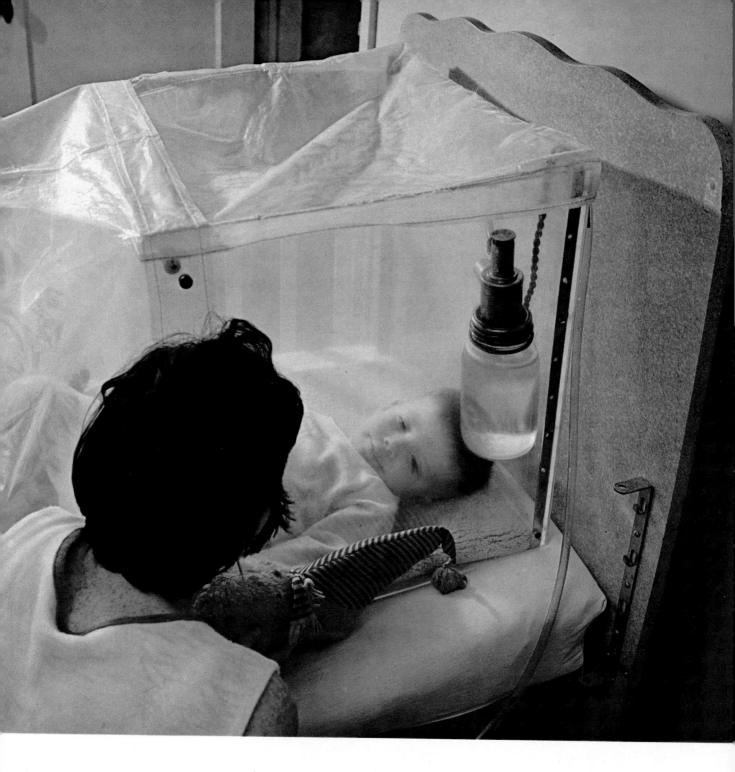

Disarming a Killer of Children

Now that antibiotics have all but eliminated pneumonia and tuberculosis as childhood killers, the respiratory disease pediatricians are most concerned with is cystic fibrosis. This ailment, carried as a recessive genetic trait by normal parents, attacks the lungs by upsetting the chemistry of the glands producing mucus. Very sticky mucus is produced; it clogs the lungs and intestines, and leads to infection and serious tissue damage.

Before the introduction of antibiotics, doctors could only watch their patients die in infancy of constant infection. The new drugs, inhaled as a vapor, soften the mucus, making it possible to prevent infection and prolong victims' lives. Because cystic fibrosis also affects the sweat glands, simple tests help detect the disease in infancy and allow doctors to start treatment before irreversible lung-tissue damage has been done.

135

HEMOPHILIAC DOGS
Rare hemophiliac Irish setters at Chapel Hill, North Carolina, living in virtual isolation to avoid injury which would cause bleeding, listen to the sound of music piped in over the loudspeaker at right. Music relieves the anxiety of isolation, which may aggravate bleeding. These dogs were used in experiments that helped establish the safety of treatment by transfusions of plasma.

"Disease of Kings" and Common Men

Hemophilia, which afflicted several of history's royal families, has always been known as "the disease of kings." But it is by no means confined to royalty; 100,000 Americans have hemophilia, and the number is growing. Hemophilia is a blood disorder which is inherited by males from their mothers. A hemophiliac's blood lacks a vital clotting ingredient. The worst effects of the disease come, not from an accidental cut, but from internal bleeding into the joints, particularly of the knees, where the accumulating blood can cause pain and severe crippling. Anything can start this bleeding, from a bad fall to a short walk across the living room. The most effective treatment is transfusions of fresh or frozen plasma, which supplies the missing clotting ingredient. Leg braces help by straightening the limbs and lessening the body's weight on the knees. But the most intriguing potential weapon against hemophilia is the patient's own emotions: it has been proved that emotional stress can worsen the bleeding tendency.

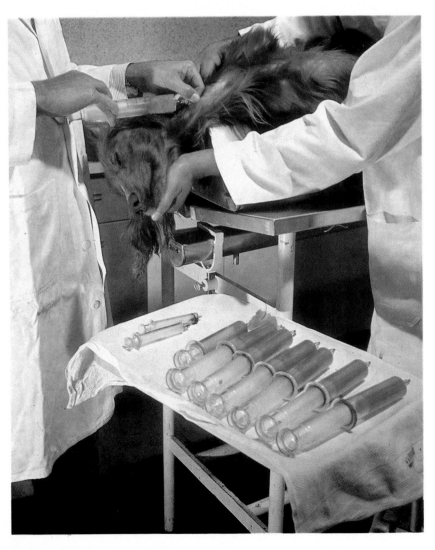

PROTECTED BY BRACES
At his clinic in New York, Dr. Henry Jordan, a pioneer in the orthopedic treatment of hemophilia, examines braces on a 17-year-old patient. The leg braces have effectively prevented crippling in this boy. A brace on his arm supports the shoulder joint, another area affected.

A LIFE-GIVING TRANSFUSION
Using plasma from a normal dog, doctors give a transfusion to a hemophiliac setter. Like humans, canine hemophiliacs lack a single blood protein, and must be guarded against injury. Human victims of this disease need frequent plasma transfusions—at five dollars to $30 apiece.

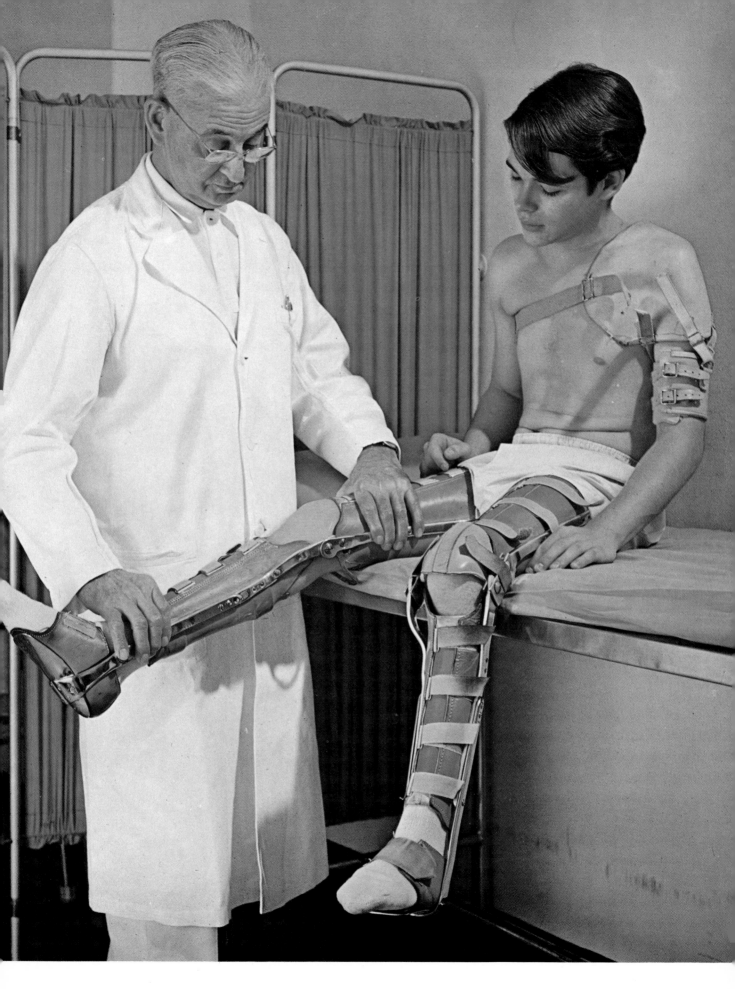

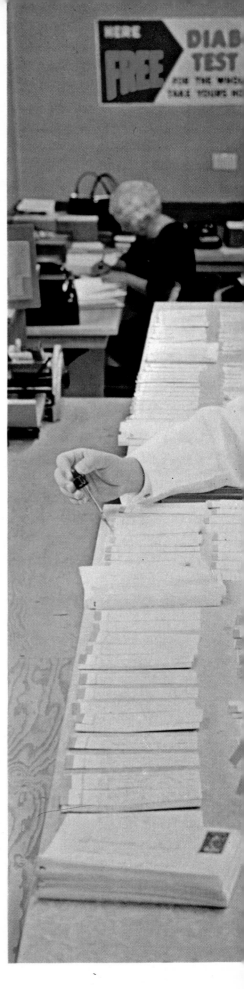

A Sentence of Death Commuted

The lucky discovery of insulin in 1921 by Charles Best *(left)* and Frederick Banting changed the character of diabetes almost overnight from a sentence of certain death to a condition that can be safely controlled if discovered in time. Diabetes is a chronic, inherited disorder of the pancreas, which manufactures a hormone that enables the body to utilize sugar properly. A shortage of this hormone, insulin, in the system of a diabetic, can result in coma and death. But a diabetic can live a relatively normal life so long as he eats a special diet and receives regular doses of insulin containing the vital protein. As of the mid-1960s there were approximately 3,400,000 diabetics living in the U.S., of whom nearly half were unaware that they had the condition.

A PIONEER IN DIABETES RESEARCH
Dr. Charles Best, shown in his Toronto University laboratory in 1964, was one of the discoverers of insulin. In 1921, Best and Frederick Banting experimented with dogs whose pancreases had been removed and who were thus diabetic. Insulin from a healthy dog saved them.

MOBILE TESTING LABORATORY
In Detroit, a line forms for diabetes blood tests outside a mobile van. Those whose tests indicated diabetes were advised to take more tests. Diabetes is often accompanied by clear-cut symptoms—including weight loss and ravenous appetite—but the search for hidden cases is complicated by the fact that the disease can be present without any apparent symptoms.

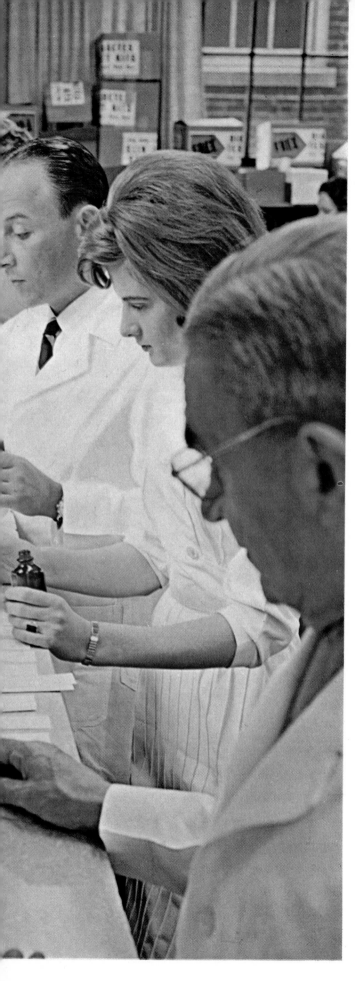

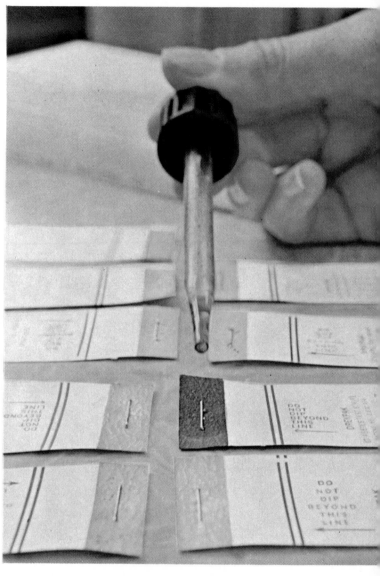

SPOTTING THE DISEASE
In a close-up of the specimen cards shown at left, a technician squeezes a chemical reagent onto the specimen strip. If the strip turns greenish-blue, it means the sender has sugar in his urine, a strong indication that he has diabetes. He will be mailed a card recommending that he undergo further free tests for the condition.

A NEW TECHNIQUE FOR TESTING
In St. Louis, technicians at a local branch of the American Diabetes Association test dried urine specimens for signs of diabetes. The specimens are sent in by people who have asked for the special kits, which consist of a card with a strip of preservative at one end. The cards make it feasible to test large numbers of people by mail.

139

MEMORY OF A SEIZURE

How it feels to have an epileptic seizure is indicated in the drawing above, which was made
by a victim of grand mal. Many epileptics have
visual premonitions of an oncoming seizure,
called "auras." These experiences resemble
dreams, although the patient is still fully conscious. Terrifying as it often is, an aura can help
steel an epileptic for the ordeal of a seizure.

Needless Burdens of Epilepsy

One of the most mysterious aspects of hereditary diseases is that not all of them involve a clear-cut genetic pattern. Researchers believe that in epilepsy—a group of disorders of the brain chemistry which produces seizures—only a predisposition for the disease is passed along from generation to generation. The onset of the disease itself, usually in childhood or adolescence, may also be caused by a severe head injury, or a variety of infections ranging from measles to spinal meningitis.

Of the estimated one million epileptics in the U.S., 80 per cent can be partially or completely relieved of seizures by a combination of drugs. But the major problems of epileptics —particularly among the 500,000 who get no treatment at all—arise from public ignorance which results in social stigma and outmoded, restrictive laws. In 17 states, epileptics can be sterilized against their will—and in some cases sterilization is mandatory. Many schools and colleges bar epileptics. And most companies, unaware of recent advances in the field, refuse to hire them. And though the ranks of epileptics have included such great figures as Mohammed and the composer Berlioz, federal laws forbid epileptics to immigrate into the U.S.

DRUGS TO STOP SEIZURES
Using a combination of the drugs shown above, an epileptic has a good chance of being able to lead a normal life. Doctors first identify the type of seizure the epileptic has, then try different drugs until they find the right combination.

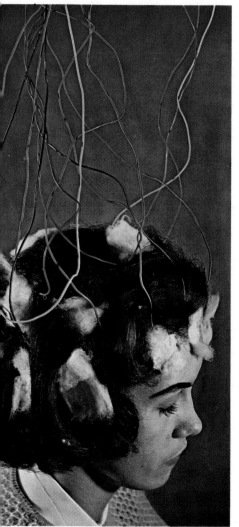

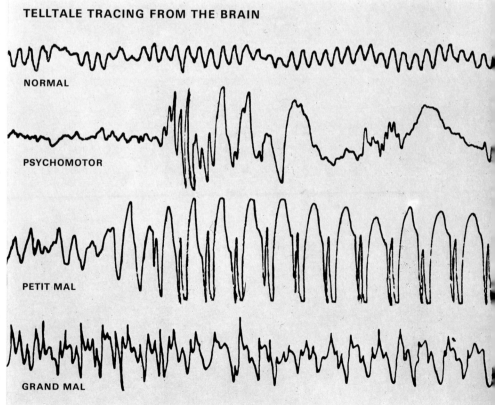

TELLTALE TRACING FROM THE BRAIN

NORMAL

PSYCHOMOTOR

PETIT MAL

GRAND MAL

THE THREE TRACKS OF EPILEPSY
A crucial first step in the treatment of epilepsy is identifying which of the three main types of seizure the patient has. Doctors accomplish this with an electroencephalograph machine. They attach small, painless, metal electrodes to the patient's skull *(left)*. The electrical waves given off by the brain are magnified by the machine and recorded on moving paper *(above)*. The most frequent and severe epilepsy is grand mal —"the falling sickness"—which involves blackouts and convulsions. Petit mal produces momentary blackouts, with facial twitching and a blank expression. Psychomotor epilepsy dims consciousness and often produces brief amnesia.

Patterns of Knowledge to Come

All the diseases shown on the previous pages probably result from "inborn errors of metabolism"—inherited malfunctions of certain body chemicals. Medical research is just beginning to attack the problem of identifying these chemicals—often proteins—to determine how they fail, using methods such as those shown here.

But the chemicals are only a part of the question of hereditary disease. At the heart of the problem are the genes, which regulate the hereditary mechanism and issue the biochemical instructions that tell the body how to grow and nourish itself. In many cases of hereditary disease, genes containing faulty instructions are traceable in a family over many generations. But in a significant number of cases where genetic disorders have recently appeared, there is no previous family history. This means that genes are spontaneously changing, or mutating. Some researchers believe this runaway mutation is influenced by new and rapidly changing environmental factors such as drugs and radiation. But whatever the cause, scientists believe that they may one day be able to control the biochemical behavior of the genes themselves—and eventually root out the menace of hereditary disease.

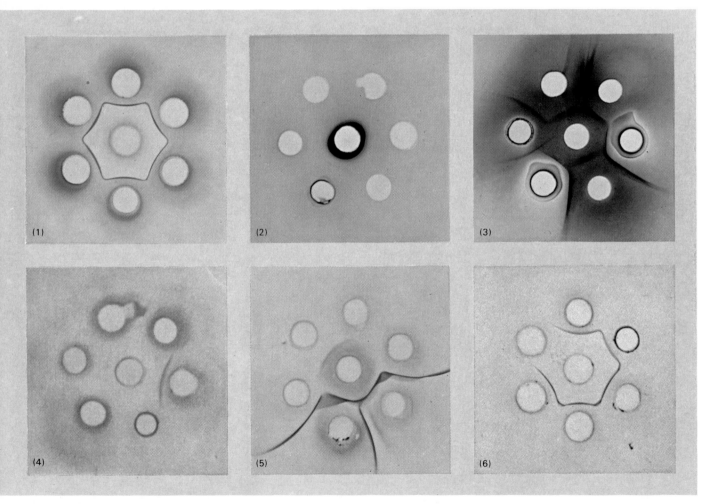

(1) (2) (3)
(4) (5) (6)

HEREDITY REVEALED IN HEXAGONS

This grouping of hexagons is actually a series of photographs of a dramatic new test designed to show the presence or absence of specific proteins in blood. Each block shows samples of blood protein from six different people (outer circles) gathered around an antibody (center circle). Where all six proteins are normal (1), a line forms about the antibody. In plates 2, 3, 4 and 5, some mysterious variations have been detected. In 6, a specific protein is missing, indicated by the broken hexagon. Researchers hope such tests will clarify the behavior of genes.

THE PATTERNS OF PROTEIN

Basic types of blood protein, taken from a number of people, show three distinct patterns (within the narrow strips). One or another of these is found in nearly every human, and they are inherited. These precise testing techniques may offer clues to the nature of genetic diseases.

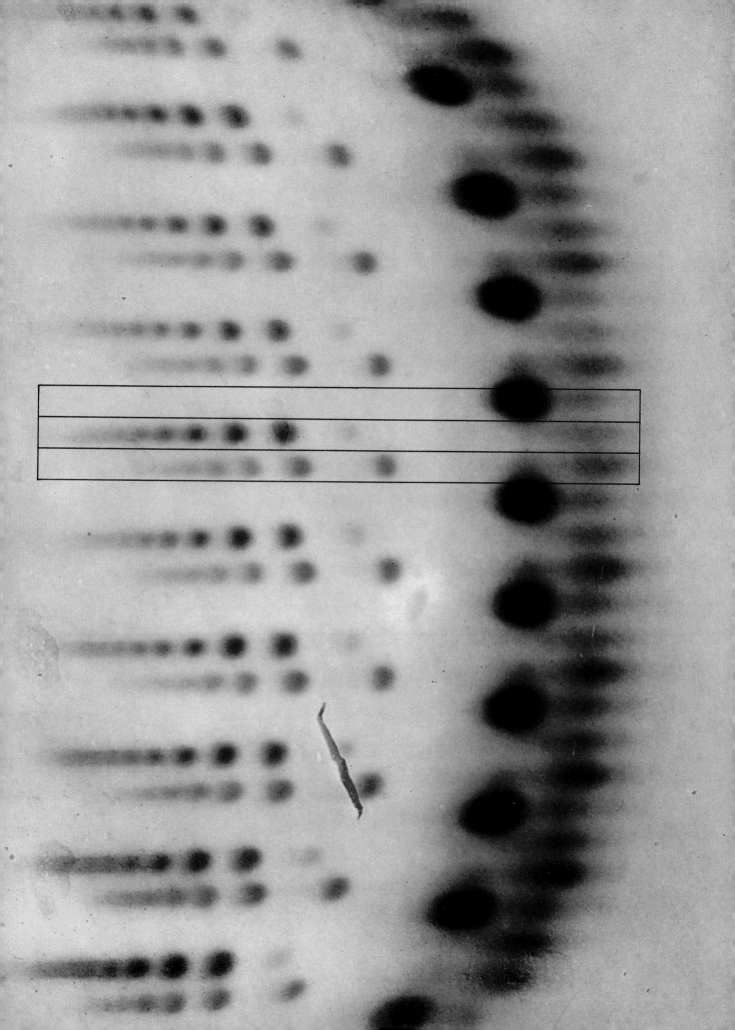

7
The Stresses
of Life

DRIVING A CAR through heavy traffic, working at a frustrating job, watching a child struggle with illness, quarreling with one's mate—the stresses of life take infinitely varied forms. And they can pose just as much of a challenge to health as bacteria, viruses, malnutrition, or chemical and physical forces.

Each man meets this challenge in his own way. The family quarrel that triggers a heart attack in one may only make another resentful, while for a third it may even serve as a goad to useful and productive work. Whatever the response, it involves the whole person; both body and mind play a part in dealing with the stresses of life. "Everyone recognizes the influence of emotion upon the flow of tears, the secretion of sweat, the color of the face, the temperature of the hands," says internist Dr. David P. Barr. "Everyone knows the racing heart of excitement, the gasp of horror, the panting of passion. . . . In a resentful man, the effect of the situation which rouses his resentment will be portrayed in his nose, his stomach, his urinary tract, his posture, and the sour look on his face. The entire organism reacts to an environment which it has interpreted as threatening."

These reactions have both physical and psychological aspects. The physical effects that result are dictated in part by the stimulus itself and in part by past experience. Everyone sneezes if sufficient plant pollen is introduced into his nasal passages—this universal physical response has the effect of eliminating the pollen from the body. But in some people this response is very much exaggerated. Because of their genetic endowment and the effects of previous exposures, these people are allergic. They find pollen so threatening that they overreact to it, throwing up a defense that produces all the symptoms of a disease—stuffed noses, itching eyes, sneezing, weeping. The symbolic meaning a situation has can also play a part in determining a physical response. For some hay fever victims, for example, the very idea that pollen is present can produce illness: one allergist arbitrarily raised the figures on the pollen-count chart in his waiting room and found that several of his patients immediately developed severe symptoms. These people had become so conditioned that they responded physically to the mere symbol of the thing they feared.

The intensity of these conditioned responses depends not only on the conscious meanings that people assign to their experiences, but on their significance to the unconscious mind as well. As Sigmund Freud showed half a century ago, no man is really aware of all the events that shaped his patterns of behavior or response to the events of adult life, since much of this conditioning takes place in early childhood, when events have a disproportionately great influence.

The enormous importance of very early experiences has been dem-

A MODERN PREDICAMENT
The tensions of 20th Century life have created a new environment for man, profoundly affecting his physical well-being. Cartoonist Robert Osborne sees a modern couple making a tense journey across harrowing terrain: even the tasks of raising and supporting children have become perilous. The parents may well suffer ulcers or drop off from a heart attack along the way.

onstrated by recent experiments with animals. Apparently the experiences of life begin to leave their stamp on the organism even before birth. Pregnant rats exposed in laboratory experiments to extreme crowding or barrages of loud noise gave birth to nervous offspring whose teeth tended to chatter and who were slower than their contemporaries in learning to run a maze. Moreover, when the experimenters transferred one group of such babies to foster mothers which had not been subjected to these experiences, the infants remained abnormal. Since many substances can pass from the maternal to the fetal bloodstream by means of the placenta, hormonal and metabolic changes in the mother rats may well have affected the unborn children. If this is the case, there may be a germ of truth in the old wives' tales about prenatal influences and "maternal impressions."

Stimulation and survival

But if too much stress is dangerous, lack of stimulation seems to be equally harmful. Some degree of stimulation—both sensory and social—is apparently essential to normal development, as well as to normal function. In sensory-deprivation experiments, volunteers who spend only 48 hours lying motionless in dark and soundless rooms begin to suffer from hallucinations and from such motor disturbances as twitching and tics. Shipwrecked sailors have been known to suffer all kinds of mental and physical derangements after long isolation on desert islands. The same kind of deprivation explains why solitary confinement has always been considered a particularly severe form of punishment.

When a baby is born, its mother instinctively cuddles it, rocks it, makes noises at it, tickles it. Although she may not know it, her behavior apparently plays an important part in helping her infant grow. In the early 1940s, psychiatrist René Spitz began a study of two sets of infants who ranged in age from a few months to one year old when the study began. One set lived in a foundling home, the other in the nursery of a prison in which their mothers were inmates. In the foundling home the babies' cribs were separated from one another by partitions, while in the prison they were not; and in the foundling home one nurse cared for seven or more children, while in the prison the babies were in the hands of their delinquent mothers all day.

Although the level of medical care was the same in both institutions, Dr. Spitz found striking differences in the two groups' resistance to disease. Over a three-year period, the prison nursery did not have a single mortality. In the foundling home, however, more than one third of the babies died. Furthermore, all the prison babies developed normally in height and weight, and all of them learned to walk, talk, eat and dress themselves at the appropriate ages. The foundling-home youngsters, on the other hand, were retarded in every respect, and most did not learn these skills at all. Nor, it developed, could this retardation be reversed. When the foundling-home babies reached 16 months of age, they were moved into a large, sunny room, without partitions, where several nurses were present all day to play with them and care for them. But the change to this more normal atmosphere had occurred too late. Instead of getting better, the children got progressively worse.

Similar evidence has been obtained with laboratory animals. Stroking and handling newborn rats for only 10 minutes a day helped them grow better, too. This was at first interpreted as another evidence of the need for tender, loving care. But when the same results were obtained by tossing the infant rats in the air, and even by giving them mild electric shocks, the experimenters realized that the handling had a salutary effect for a somewhat different reason: it satisfied the animals' need for stimulation. Rats thus treated were larger, more active, less nervous and better able to learn than animals that were not stimulated. Moreover, the handled animal was also more resistant to starvation and infection. Recent studies have shown that rats handled only a few minutes a day in infancy grow up to resist situations so stressful that they produce heart damage and intestinal ulcers in other adult rats.

The purpose of mother love

Thus a mother's fondling of her baby may serve a purpose she never intended. "We may suppose," suggests W. R. Thompson, a Wesleyan University psychologist, "that the mother gives her newborn infant love only from her standpoint, and simply sensory stimulation from his."

As the child develops and becomes able to discriminate between stimuli, however, the specific quality of the stimulation becomes more important. The caress his mother gives takes on a meaning far beyond any stimulating effect it may have. And soon even her smile becomes a highly significant cue, calling for certain specific responses.

Throughout man's life, most of the responses he makes are to such symbols and cues. No longer does he have to contend with tigers, snakes, extreme cold, lack of food and other physical dangers. Instead he must deal with schedules, traffic, noise, crowding, competition and other stressful situations imposed by man on man.

Depending on the meaning of these stresses to him, man's reaction to them may be out of all proportion to the dangers they actually present, as a recent experiment with a jet pilot demonstrated.

Hooked to an apparatus that was registering his blood pressure, the pilot sat in the cockpit of an F-100 ready to take off, when a mechanical difficulty developed that forced him to wait. For the next four hours, while technicians tried to find out what was wrong, the pilot remained

A NIGHTMARE OF FRUSTRATION, the traffic jam satirized in this drawing by the artist Boris Artzybasheff is just one of the annoyances that repeatedly confront modern man. The toll in terms of stress is great. Accumulating through the years, pent-up tensions may finally cause increased irritability, mental illness and even organic disease.

in the cockpit, becoming increasingly annoyed. Not only was he angry at the delay and concerned lest all the preparations be wasted, but he seemed to observers to blame himself for the trouble. Normally, his blood pressure at rest was 120 to 130 systolic (as the heart contracts) and 70 to 80 diastolic (as the heart relaxes). But now, as his frustration mounted so did his blood pressure, which climbed to 220 systolic and 150 diastolic.

Finally the difficulty with the apparatus was corrected and the flight got under way. Once in the air, the pilot's blood pressure went down to 180 over 110—a good deal lower than during the strain of waiting. It rose above this only during intentional stall maneuvers and during preparations for landing, both relatively risky procedures.

Another pilot, connected to similar apparatus, sat in the cab of a centrifuge, awaiting the start of an experiment designed to test the effect of gravity forces on the body. While he was waiting, he happened to overhear one of the test engineers make a sarcastic remark which he took personally. Immediately his blood pressure shot up from 130/80 to 180/120.

Stress on the sidelines

In a study of stress at the Harvard Medical School, physiological tests were given to the members of the varsity crew during practice sessions, as well as before and after the Harvard-Yale race. It was expected that the terrific physical effort of practice sessions along the race course would produce considerable evidence of stress, but the oarsmen's response was not as great as might have been expected. The morning before the race, however, the indications of stress began to rise. In the excitement of the race, these indications climbed to extreme heights, and the crewmen finished up completely exhausted. More surprising, their coach, who had been watching from the sidelines, showed as much evidence of stress as the crew.

In any emergency, the overall response of the body generally falls into what has been called the "fight-or-flight" pattern, in which a series of internal changes occur that prepare the body for vigorous effort and for the effects of injury. As described by Walter B. Cannon in 1915, the fight-or-flight response releases quantities of epinephrine into the bloodstream. This additional epinephrine serves a number of purposes. It calls forth stored carbohydrates from the liver, thus flooding the body with sugar for energy; it helps in distributing blood to the heart, lungs, central nervous system and limbs; it quickly abolishes the effects of muscular fatigue; and it makes the blood coagulate more readily, so that less will be lost in case of injury. All these changes are associated with elemental emotional experiences of pain, fear and rage. "The facts at once have significance if considered in relation to the struggle for existence," Cannon wrote. "If fear always paralyzed it would result only in danger of destruction. But fear and aggressive feeling, as anticipatory responses to critical situations, make ready for action and thereby they have had great survival value."

Later research has amplified Cannon's findings. It has been learned, for example, that in addition to sugar, fat is mobilized to produce the energy to fuel exertion. And other hormones besides epinephrine are released into the blood. Many of these reactions, like those discovered by Cannon, are intended to prepare the body for vigorous physical activity.

Such activity was, of course, commonplace in the early days of the race. To survive in a hunting and gathering society, men had to be always on the move and always alert to defend themselves against damage. The development of an agricultural civilization permitted men to establish permanent homes, but still required them to do heavy physical labor. It is only in very recent times that men have been able to live with a minimum of physical exertion. In fact, the emergence of urban civilization makes it virtually impossible to relieve tensions by taking physical action. In today's environment, some of the biological equipment that was necessary in earlier times may have become obsolete. It may even be a handicap. As physiologist David A. Hamburg puts it, "The contemporary human organism frequently gets mobilized for exertion but ends up doing little or nothing—preparation for action, without action."

The price of politeness

This is a little like running the motor at full blast while keeping the brake on; if it is done too often, something must give. If, for example, the fat mobilized during a fight-or-flight response is not burned up by violent activity, it may be deposited in the arteries to form the characteristic plaques of atherosclerosis—at least in people whose genetic endowment predisposes them to it. In the long run it may have been healthier for men to let off steam by punching each other in the old-fashioned way— so long as they survived—than to behave according to the more civilized mores of today.

Russian scientists have repeatedly produced symptoms of atherosclerosis and hypertension in chimpanzees by subjecting them to experiences that made them violently—and helplessly—jealous. Several times they have conducted experiments in which a male chimpanzee who had been living happily with his several wives in a large compound was suddenly taken away from them and placed in a screened cage from which he could see them but not reach them. Then a vigorous young male was introduced into the compound to enjoy the females and become lord of the territory. Screaming with rage, the first male had to witness it all

PHYSICAL THREAT

PHYSICAL TRIUMPH

EMOTIONAL THREAT

RESPONDING TO A THREAT, early man *(top)* underwent a variety of physical reactions —such as a rise in blood pressure and an increase in adrenal secretion—which gave him the extra strength to conquer his enemies *(center).* Civilized man *(bottom)* faces more complex threats with the same old physical system, yet he is rarely called upon to meet stress with physical action. His body prepares him for a battle that is never fought. The result: damage to his system.

149

with impotent fury. Within three months he was dead of severe athero-sclerosis and hypertension.

Blood pressure that rises in response to emergency may persist at its high level long after the threat is over. After two years of fighting during the Libyan campaign of World War II—chasing Marshal Rommel in the desert, being chased, and chasing him again—the Allied armies won the final battle, and 700 men who had participated in virtually the entire campaign were sent off to a seaside resort to rest and relax. As late as two months after the final battle, the group still registered unusually high blood pressures.

The adaptable rats

The fight-or-flight reactions described by Cannon were specifically directed toward violent physical activity. A quarter century after Cannon drew this picture of man's responses to emergencies, Dr. Hans Selye, then a young researcher at McGill University in Montreal, discovered that experimental animals showed physical responses to other types of stimuli as well. Whatever he did to his experimental animals—whether he shot epinephrine or insulin into them, whether he exposed them to extreme cold or extreme heat or X-rays or physical injuries—they always underwent certain physiological changes, and these changes always followed the same pattern. In addition to the specific reactions—burns, for example, and injuries—a complex sequence of nonspecific responses could always be seen. Among these were an increased secretion of adrenal-cortical hormones, and an abrupt decrease in the number of eosinophils, a type of blood cell. These responses comprise the first stage of what Dr. Selye calls the general adaptation syndrome. He pointed out that it could be brought about by any stressful situation, from the emotional tension produced by crossing a busy intersection as well as by any physical stimulus.

The late Dr. Harold G. Wolff advanced a theory that may explain the role of stress in the development of disease. According to him, the body reacts to stresses—emotional as well as physical—by choosing from a limited repertoire of standard, built-in mechanisms of response associated with the organ systems used in satisfying such basic needs as those for food and elimination. Since these responses may not be relevant to the immediate situation, they may disturb homeostasis rather than help restore it. They may even be more damaging than the original threat. Disease is often primarily the manifestation of such an unsuitable response, particularly when this response is prolonged or often repeated.

For example, it has long been known that the stomach lining responds to emotional disturbances, and that people subjected to such disturbances tend to get stomach ulcers as a consequence. The stomach's response was seen with astounding clarity in a man known to medical literature simply as "Tom." When Tom was nine years old, he damaged his gullet so severely, by drinking steaming-hot clam chowder, that it no longer functioned. The subsequent operation that enabled him to eat left him with nearly four and a half inches of stomach protruding through the skin of his abdomen. For the rest of his life, Tom fed himself by chewing up his food and spitting it into a funnel attached to a tube that carried it to the exposed portion of his stomach. He kept his condition a secret from all but his closest friends and family until a severe anemia sent him to the hospital when he was 53 years old. There Dr. Wolff and his colleague, Dr. Stewart Wolf, recognizing the unusual opportunity Tom represented, talked him into becoming a walking laboratory, and for several years they made the most of the "window" in Tom's stomach.

Whenever Tom felt threatened or angry—as on one occasion when he was accused of ineffectiveness and worried that he would be fired from his job—his stomach lining flushed, its capillaries filled with blood, and his secretion of digestive juices increased, eating away at the normally thick layer of mucus that protected the lining. If his resentment persisted, further changes occurred. The capillaries in his engorged stomach lining became extremely fragile, and bleeding developed at several points on its folds. Such a condition may be the precursor of a peptic ulcer.

A response of anger or hunger

In a way, Tom's stomach was behaving like that of a man who is preparing for a meal: engorgment of the stomach lining and increased secretion of gastric juices are typical reactions to the prospect of food. As Dr. Stewart Wolf pointed out, such reactions, although inappropriate to a man like Tom, might have been appropriate in the earliest period of man's evolution, when the way to cope with an opponent was to kill and eat him.

When Tom was depressed or withdrawn, on the other hand, his stomach lining became bloodless and pale. Hardly any digestive juices flowed out. Even the sight and smell of food failed to stir up any normal digestive activity.

The window in Tom's stomach thus allowed objective observations of the relationship between emotional states and the functioning of the stomach. Every day Tom arrived to have his stomach examined, after a night of fasting, and every day he talked with his physicians about the latest events in his personal life and at work, together with his attitudes and feelings toward them. Often his stomach revealed emotional conflicts even before Tom acknowledged their existence.

While these observations showed that stressful situations and excessive secretion of digestive juices set the stage for the development of ulcers, they did not demonstrate the conditions under which this illness actually develops. Judging by recent experiments with monkeys, a crucial factor is the timing of the periods of emotional stress and those of rest.

While teaching monkeys to avoid electric shocks by pressing a lever, scientists at the Walter Reed Army Institute of Research were surprised to find that a large number of the animals died. Moreover, the autopsies showed that they had perished of ailments very rare in laboratory monkeys—ulcers and other gastrointestinal damage. To make sure that the ulcers had not developed as a result of the electric shocks, the researchers undertook another experiment. They paired off several monkeys, in such a way that both members of each pair received shocks but only one could prevent them. The "executive" monkeys, those forced to make the decision, soon learned what was required of them; thereafter, as long as the current was on, they pressed their levers as often as 20 times a minute to avoid being shocked, and only occasionally were they slow enough to receive a jolt. Their partners, on the other hand, soon lost interest in pressing their dummy levers, and resigned themselves to going along with the executives' decisions. After three weeks of this schedule, the decision-making monkeys died of perforated ulcers. Their partners remained in good health.

Timetable for ulcers

In this first series of tests, the periods of rest and shock had alternated every six hours. In an effort to speed up the ulcer-making process, the experimenters changed the timing, putting some monkeys on an 18-hours-on, six-hours-off schedule. In this situation, one of the executive monkeys contracted tuberculosis, to which monkeys in captivity appear to be particularly susceptible, and died after a few weeks. But the others went right on pressing their levers day after day, week after week, without developing any abnormalities whatsoever. On an even tighter schedule—30 minutes on, 30 minutes off—they remained equally healthy. Only the original six-hour schedule produced ulcers. Apparently, the experimenters concluded, ulcers develop only after intermittent emotional stress, and only when the timing of the periods of stress coincides with some yet unexplained rhythm of the body.

But why should stresses make one organ of the body succumb and not any other? The stricken organ, Harold Wolff pointed out, is not necessarily weak or inferior; it may be especially well developed and strong. Nevertheless it may be unable to cope with an ever bigger burden. Tendencies to react preferentially with one organ or organ system, Wolff said, "are apparently deeply ingrained, since they occur in any individuals of the same stock under analogous conditions. It seems likely that they are stockbound, analogous to the retriever patterns in dogs, running pattern in horses, hoarding in squirrels. . . . An individual may have been a po-

A PEPTIC ULCER forms when acid gastric juices—overproduced during periods of stress —eat into the stomach wall. The acid first erodes the inner membrane, forming a lesion called an acute ulcer. This ulcer may heal, but if the acid is chronically overproduced, it eventually eats into the deeper muscle layer. At last it may perforate the stomach wall entirely, permitting gastric juices to flow directly into the abdomen. Without prompt surgical attention, perforation may cause death.

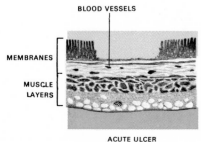

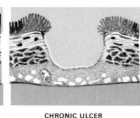

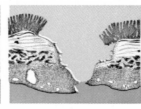

ACUTE ULCER   CHRONIC ULCER   PERFORATION

BLOOD VESSELS

MEMBRANES

MUSCLE LAYERS

tential 'nose reactor' or 'colon reactor' all his life without ever actually having called upon a particular protective pattern for sustained periods because he did not need to."

Although most people have colds from time to time, some people seem particularly susceptible to them. Apparently, the nasal mucosa of such "nose reactors" is especially sensitive and becomes easily engorged—sometimes because of temperature shifts or other irritants, often because of changes in mood. As a result, these people fall ill from infections that would not trouble their neighbors.

The happy road to health

Difficult life situations often lead to increased susceptibility to illness. In various groups of workers studied by Dr. Lawrence Hinkle, the healthiest were those who felt that their aspirations for marriage, home and job were generally satisfied. Those whose marriages were disrupted, who were burdened with responsibility, or who felt their work to be frustrating and had no hope of escape, had the highest incidence of illness.

In those cases, the determining factor was not the objective situation, but its meaning to the person involved. A man reacts to his social environment as he perceives it, and the same environment may have diametrically opposed meaning to different people, even within the framework of the same general culture. Some men flourish on the freedom of retirement, for example, while others find it much more stressful than working at a regular job. Indeed, so many have found it traumatic that doctors speak of "retirement disease" as a recognized medical entity which can even lead to an early death.

Even the pain associated with such purely physical things as wounds can be influenced by the significance of the wound to its victims. While attending soldiers wounded on the Anzio beachhead in Italy during World War II, Dr. Henry Beecher, later Professor of Research in Anesthesia at Harvard, noticed that only one quarter of the men who had been severely hurt felt enough pain to ask for any help. They were not in shock, and had been given no morphine. But some of them may have considered their wounds a blessing in disguise. For these men, the war was over, and they were soon to be shipped home. In civilian life, by contrast, some three quarters of patients recovering from the smaller wounds of surgery complain of severe pain and ask for relief—probably because illness and surgery represent unmitigated evils to them.

The almost magical power of placebos—chemically valueless pills or sham medical procedures—is further evidence that when man changes his assessment of a situation, he also changes his physiological response to it. The word "placebo" means "I shall please" in Latin; it was used in the 15th Century as a synonym for flattery or a flatterer, and later for a courtesy designed to soothe or gratify. Ever since medicine adopted them, placebos have repeatedly helped patients to feel better; no matter what the placebo or how it is used, it achieves positive effects in approximately 35 per cent of cases, relieving the pain of such diverse conditions as operative wounds and angina pectoris. Recently, experiments have shown that placebos can produce real measurable changes in the functioning of the pulmonary, gastrointestinal and urogenital systems.

"When the doctor becomes the treatment"

Belief in one's physician can in itself be a strong factor in recovery from illness. Many medical men have witnessed the "miraculous moment . . . when the doctor becomes the treatment," as the late Dr. Alan Gregg, of The Rockefeller Foundation, put it. Even medically valueless surgery can have this placebo effect. Dr. Beecher has reported several cases in which patients with angina pectoris—pain in the chest that results from defective circulation to the heart—showed dramatic and measurable improvement after receiving a mere skin incision because they were under the impression that an operation had been performed. Before the pseudo-operation, one man with advanced heart disease could do test exercises for only four minutes; he had to stop because of severe pain, and readings of his cardiogram strongly suggested that something was wrong. After the skin incision he was able to exercise for 10 minutes with no pain, and his cardiogram gave no cause for concern. "It is clear," Dr. Beecher writes, "that not only drugs, but also a procedure—surgery—has placebo effects."

Perhaps the most dramatic illustrations of the ways in which psychic processes can affect man's physiology come from studies of hypnosis. The use of hypnosis to reduce pain is well known; a number of physicians and dentists employ it as an anesthetic in surgery. According to a report published in 1959, hypnotic suggestion actually controlled the amount of damage inflicted by burns on the arms of volunteers in an experiment. Subjected to burns while they were in the normal waking state, all of them suffered almost identical injuries on both arms. Then they were placed in a hypnotic trance, and the suggestion was made that their left arms would be impervious to heat while their right arms would be particularly vulnerable to it. Although identical amounts of heat were used in each case, the suggestion was effective in 30 out of the 40 subjects: when burned they showed little damage on their left arms and considerable damage on their right.

The power of suggestion can also work in negative ways, leading to the kind of discouragement and despondency seen in responses of withdrawal. Here, as opposed to the fight-or-flight responses, the whole organism appears to slow down. The word "petrified" would not be inappropriate to describe what happens to the body in this state. There is a virtual absence of gastric secretions and a sharp reduction in motor activity; all the systems of the body seem to sleep. Although the mechanism of withdrawal is not well understood, many real examples seem to exist, the most extreme one being the phenomenon of voodoo deaths.

Among the aborigines of Australia, for instance, any man who breaks a tribal taboo may be punished by a ritual called "pointing the bone." In this procedure, the medicine man points a bone in the direction of the culprit, who then believes himself bewitched and without hope of survival. For a few moments, the "boned" man stands aghast, his muscles twitching. He attempts to shriek, but the sound freezes in his throat. As his horror deepens, he may sway backward and fall to the ground, moaning and writhing as if in mortal agony. Then he resigns himself to his fate, a dreadful composure comes over him, and he quietly crawls away. From this point on, reports an eyewitness, "he sickens and frets, refusing to eat and keeping aloof from the daily affairs of the tribe. . . . His death is only a matter of a comparatively short time."

The quitter rats

Similar withdrawal behavior has been observed in animals. In fights among wild rats, for example, the loser often lies down, weakens and dies, although he shows no evidence of injury. "A series of bouts may leave an attacked wild rat in a state of collapse," writes zoologist S. A. Barnett, "while the dominant attacker shows no distress. . . . Both rats have leapt wildly about; neither, perhaps, is wounded; yet the effects on the two antagonists are in complete contrast."

There may be a connection between such deaths and the fact noted by Dr. R. S. Fisher, Coroner of the City of Baltimore, that a number of Americans die each year after taking poison in doses so small it could not in itself cause death, or after inflicting small, nonlethal wounds on themselves. Apparently they die as a result of a belief in their doom. As every doctor knows, one of the most important requirements for health in any patient is his will to live.

The knowledge that mind and body interact is not new. During the Middle Ages, for example, both physical and mental illnesses were treated by ministering to the whole person, through that part of him that theology called his "soul." For centuries it was taken for granted that people could die of grief, that unrequited love could cause illness, that fear and anger could make men mad. But with the flowering of the germ theory of disease in the second half of the 19th Century, and with medicine's increasing interest in discovering the specific causes of specific illnesses, much of this earlier understanding of human nature and of the role of the emotions was tossed aside as "unscientific."

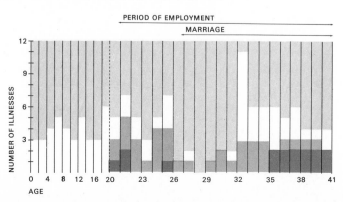

STRESS AND DISEASE are strongly linked, as this chart, based on the life history of an American workingman, demonstrates. White areas stand for minor illnesses, light-olive squares for minor illnesses that required medical attention. Dark-olive areas represent disabling diseases. From the ages of 20 to 26 this man worked his way out of a difficult homelife with his parents. At 26, employed and secure, he married. In his thirties, the illness of his wife and daughters, death of his parents and a growing burden of debt gravely affected his health.

The work of Claude Bernard, Ivan Pavlov, Walter B. Cannon, Harold G. Wolff and Hans Selye laid the foundations for the present understanding of the relation of inappropriate body responses to the development of disease; and the findings of psychiatrists and psychologists helped turn the attention of clinical medicine once again to the "whole person." In treating their patients, psychoanalysts could not help but see that the ups and downs of various illnesses often coincided with periods of conflict or calm, or that certain diseases, such as ulcers, were associated with prolonged emotional disturbances. These observations led to the development of "psychosomatic medicine" as a separate branch of the healing art, dealing with illnesses such as colitis, hypertension, coronary disease, peptic ulcers, migraine and others in which the emotional component seemed particularly significant.

The category "psychosomatic disease" is no longer as meaningful as it was considered to be a generation ago; today doctors believe that any illness can be influenced by what goes on in the mind, just as the state of the mind is always influenced by what goes on in the body. Throughout life there is a constant interplay between body and mind, and both require a certain amount of stimulation. Man functions best when the stresses of life stimulate him enough to exercise his faculties, but not so much as to harass or overwhelm him.

The Healthy Primitive

Of the 3.3 billion people in the world, a tiny minority—probably under .1 per cent—live in such isolation that they are deprived of all medical care and health knowledge. Astonishingly, they may be among the healthiest humans on earth. Although they frequently must endure some of the world's most rugged climate and terrain, they lead vigorous lives and fall prey to few of the diseases of civilization. The explanation lies partly in their very isolation. Good health depends less on medicines than on adaptation to environment—and most isolated peoples have had plenty of opportunity to come to terms with their surroundings, undisturbed by outside influences. Their bodies build up resistance to local diseases and they rarely encounter new ones. It is only when outsiders carry in strange diseases that they suffer. One Eskimo village at the turn of the century lost 98 of 99 inhabitants to measles after a visit from a "civilized" explorer.

NO GLASSES NEEDED
A young African girl, member of the Mabaan tribe of the Sudan, submits to an eye examination. She and almost every other member of her tribe were found to have perfect vision. The Mabaans live in an inhospitable land which is parched desert one half the year and impassable swamp the other half. Yet isolation has assured them a well-adjusted life and superb health.

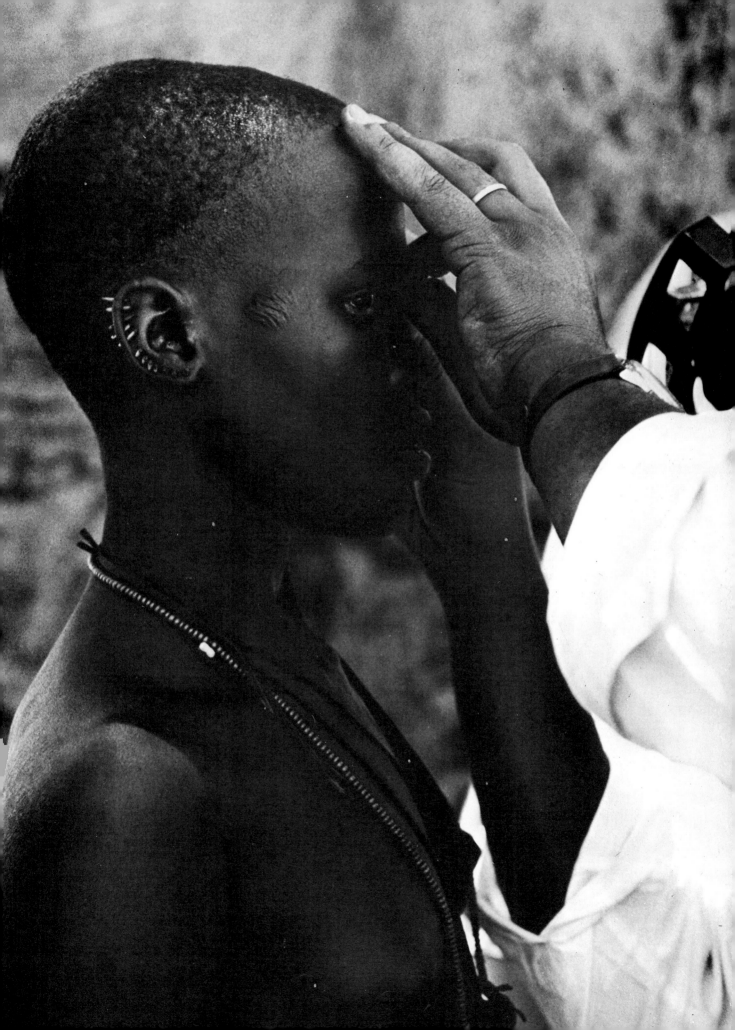

Staying Fit in the Stone Age

Jet planes flying northwest from Rio de Janeiro cast their shadows across the Mato Grosso area of central Brazil, the largest unexplored territory of the Western Hemisphere. In that land of dense jungle live some of the world's most primitive people, the group of tribes known collectively as the Xinguano Indians. The Xinguanos lead serene, Stone Age lives. They spend their days hunting, gathering food and doing some desultory farming, and they use only the simplest tools and almost no clothing.

A striking characteristic of these people is their exuberant good health. Their bodies are strong and fit, and their diet is well balanced even by modern standards. Malaria and respiratory ailments are their only major diseases, but are rarely fatal, and the Indians are seldom bothered by minor ills and infections.

Unfortunately, the Xinguanos, like many primitive peoples, have proved desperately vulnerable to unfamiliar diseases brought by the white man. In 1954 one tribe of 730 Indians was reduced to 600 by an epidemic of measles. The Brazilian Government now does its utmost to protect them from contamination. But it is almost inevitable that the germs of encroaching civilization will eventually reach them—and will all too often overpower the rude health the jungle permits.

A HEALTHY SPECIMEN
A well-muscled Camayurá Indian of Brazil's Mato Grosso fashions a sleeping hammock from palm fibers. Although as many as 30 Indians may sleep in one thatched hut, many of the infections of civilization—like tuberculosis, chicken pox and mumps—are almost unknown.

WOMAN'S WORK

A Camayurá girl prepares manioc bread, made from a potatolike root that is a staple of the Indians' diet. One explorer noted that the bread has a fascinating flavor despite a consistency like "thin rubber sponge." With manioc, the Indians eat a great deal of fish, fruit, and some meat, which gives them a well-balanced diet.

STOMPING WITH THE XAVANTE

As a round-bellied urchin looks on, men of the Xavante tribe kick up the dust in a traditional dance. The Xinguano Indians have great stamina. On hunting forays they trek tirelessly or paddle canoes for long distances through jungle and swamp. Then, during week-long feasts, they stay up most of the night dancing and singing, and still rise bright and early with the sun.

A Quiet Life
and a Long One

The woman striding along in the photograph at right is almost 80 years old. Her hearing and vision are better than most American teenagers', her teeth are sound, her heart strong. She is a Mabaan of the Sudan, and most of her fellow tribesmen are as healthy as she. One explorer noted that life in the Mabaan villages is so quiet that there is normally less noise than is made by a modern refrigerator.

The Mabaans enjoy longevity that would be remarkable in the most medically pampered society. Furthermore, their declining years are almost free of the usual degenerative diseases of old age. Scientists are still puzzled by the Mabaans' extraordinary health, but their stable, tranquil environment is almost certainly an important factor. When a Mabaan moves from home to the city of Khartoum, 650 miles away, he is beset by a host of ills he has never known before.

STAFF OF A HEALTHY LIFE
With help from her little daughter, a Mabaan mother grinds a starchy flour from millet seed known as durra. Baked, made into a thin gruel or fermented into a kind of beer, durra is the chief item of a diet that is monotonous and skimpy. Yet the Mabaans seem to thrive on it.

STILL GOING STRONG
A Mabaan matriarch enjoys a quiet smoke. In her prime, this woman's hearing was so acute she could hear someone talking 100 yards away. The Mabaans almost never have such familiar diseases of the Western countries as high blood pressure, ulcers, atherosclerosis and appendicitis.

Rising above Affliction

The Arabs shown on these pages live in a virtual pesthole of disease: the vast, sluggish marshes that cover much of southern Iraq. These swamps serve as both reservoirs and cesspools; proliferating germs and insects spread a wide spectrum of illnesses, ranging from yaws to schistosomiasis.

Inevitably many of the Marsh Arabs develop parasitic and microbial infections, but by their own lights they go right on leading a normal, healthy existence. Like many primitive peoples, they are afflicted but by no means incapacitated. In fact, medical men who have visited them believe that their life-span compares well with those of far more favored peoples.

FOOD SUPPLY AND SEWER
Balancing easily in a primitive canoe *(above)*, Marsh Arabs fish the waters of their swampy domain, which covers some 6,000 square miles. The areas of open water are relatively clean—but the narrow channels along which the Arabs build their houses are usually running sewers.

PUBLIC ENEMY NO. 1
Despite a variety of afflictions, the Arabs lead extremely active lives. Here three hunters pose in triumph with the carcass of a wild pig, their worst enemy. Armed with guns and spears, the Arabs hunt the pigs relentlessly, but are often fatally gored by their ferocious adversaries.

INDUSTRY OF THE MARSHES

A skilled artisan and his helper weave mats from the reeds that grow in profusion around them. The mats, which are used as flooring and roofing for houses, become comfortable resting places for the bats and birds that are the carriers of rabies or psittacosis, a virus disease.

A Hardy Breed in Happy Isolation

On a barren volcanic peak rising out of the South Atlantic perches what is probably the most isolated civilized community on earth, Tristan da Cunha. On their tiny 40-square-mile island, 1,300 miles from the nearest inhabited island, the hardy Tristanians have been on their own since the British colony was founded in the early 19th Century by the remnants of a military garrison and a few shipwrecked sailors.

Existence for the 270 islanders is rugged. They live mostly on fish and potatoes, and the climate is stormy and cold. Inbreeding has produced genetic disorders, and there is some anemia and asthma. Yet there are few health problems on Tristan. No major illnesses attack the islanders, no epidemics have ravaged them, and their life expectancy is longer than that of Europeans and Americans. They do not even catch colds—except when a ship visits and leaves sniffles and sore throats in its wake.

In 1961 the island's tranquil life was violently upset when the volcano erupted. The inhabitants were taken by ship to England. Many of them immediately came down with respiratory infections, and four died. Besides being plagued by colds, the transplanted islanders were further disturbed by the noise and bustle of their new environment. A year after their arrival, when the volcano had quieted, the adult Tristanians voted 148 to 5 to return and the British Government obligingly carried them back to their distant, craggy home.

LEADER OF THE CLANS
Tristan's head man, Willie Repetto, 62 *(left)*, rides a donkey to the potato fields near the island's settlement, Edinburgh. Repetto is one of only seven family names among the Tristanians. Because of repeated intermarriage, a number of Tristanians share a genetic eye defect.

A DAY ON THE RANGE

A group of Tristan men bulldog a steer. The islanders consider themselves seamen first, farmers second; the few cattle they own are usually used as draft animals rather than as a source of food. As a consequence, the diet on Tristan da Cunha is low on milk and beef.

UNHAPPY IN PICCADILLY

Looking and feeling out of place in London's Piccadilly Circus, some Tristanians *(below)* take in the unfamiliar city sights. Most of the islanders had never seen cars or tall buildings before. Interested but not impressed, they preferred the 19th Century calm of their island home.

Back home, Tristanians trudge up their island's rocky beach. Months later, they seemed to be resuming their former state of health: in Britai

they had gained some immunity to respiratory ailments; now visiting ships were again leaving behind the traditional epidemics of sniffles.

8
The Key to Survival

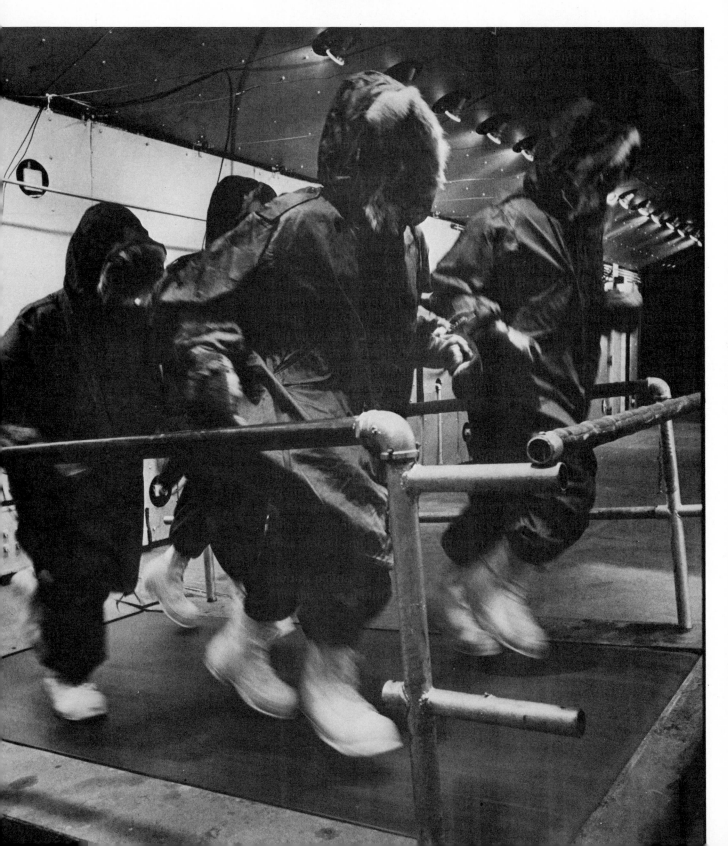

THE TRAVELER who gets off a plane at La Paz, Bolivia, is in for an unsettling experience: breathing the rarefied air of this highest big city in the world. Although his first few breaths may leave him exhilarated, talkative and happily giddy, the pleasant feeling does not last. Suddenly he may become nauseated, and develop a violent headache and a strange inability to climb even the shortest flight of stairs. If he reacts as some people do, he soon will be unable to think clearly and his memory will begin to fail him. His tongue will move with difficulty, and his feet turn icy. He may become irritable and even irrational, and his mood may swing from one extreme to another. Whatever his symptoms may be—and they are usually unpleasant—their only cure is time: it may take several weeks for his body to adapt to the high altitude.

La Paz is 11,900 feet above sea level; at this height, the air is so thin that people from lowland areas inhale only half as much oxygen as they normally do. Since they are not breathing any more quickly, their tissues are soon starved for oxygen. And because the brain is particularly susceptible to oxygen deficiency, symptoms of mental confusion are among the first to appear. Fortunately, the visitor finally adapts; he begins to breathe more deeply and his body begins to increase its production of red corpuscles, so that there are more of them to pick up the oxygen that is available. At this point, he is able to function almost normally, although his mental and emotional processes are still a little disturbed.

People who were born and raised at high altitudes suffer no such difficulties. The Indians of Morococha, a Peruvian mining town 14,900 feet up in the Andes, regularly put in long, hard days of physical labor in the mines, and in their spare time play a great deal of soccer. Comparative studies showed that they could run much longer on a treadmill in their sky-high town than could a group of Peruvian sailors who were tested in Lima at sea level. The Indians ran an average of 59 minutes before exhaustion set in, while the sailors could run for only 34 minutes.

This superior performance must be related to mechanisms of physiological adaptation that the Indians have developed: they have a larger number of red blood cells to carry oxygen to the tissues, and they breathe more quickly and more deeply, so that 20 per cent more air reaches their lungs than reaches those of people who live at sea level.

It is clear from these examples that every man is a creature of his environment, and his physical responses are powerfully influenced by the world he lives in. When he shifts to a new environment, his body makes a violent effort to adapt to the new situations that confront it. In this respect, a child born at high altitudes faces the same problems as does a visitor who has lived in a lower area. Each of them must acquire certain responses which neither had originally. Yet natural selection must

THE HARDY HUMAN
Man's adaptability is demonstrated by these U.S. soldiers, who are testing their ability to function while wearing cold-weather gear by running on treadmills against an artificial gale at −10° Fahrenheit. At this Army center in Natick, Massachusetts, men have endured temperatures ranging from −70° F. to +165° F., and wind velocities of up to 40 miles per hour.

also play a role in encouraging the reproduction of people well fitted genetically to adapt to high altitudes. People born at low altitudes have smaller rib cages than the Andean Indians. In addition it has frequently been noted that people from the lowlands become much less fertile when they move to high altitudes, while the native Indians reproduce normally.

Among the conspicuous kinds of genetic adaptation is body shape, which the anthropologist Carleton Coon has defined as the extent to which the body resembles a sphere. As Coon suggested, an elongated shape is a distinct advantage in hot, dry climates: for the volume it contains, such a shape has greater surface than a sphere, and thus provides a greater area through which to lose body heat. And in fact, tall, thin people do seem to predominate in hot, dry climates, possibly because of their selective advantage. In cold areas, on the other hand, people may tend toward a rounder shape, which conserves heat.

Even in prehistoric times, people migrated from one area to another so much that these distinctions must have become blurred. Nevertheless, some selective forces may very well have been involved in the development of the various body shapes.

Skin color provides another example of genetic adaptation. In areas with strong sunshine and clear skies, dark-skinned people have an advantage; dark pigment helps to filter out some of the more harmful solar rays. Forest dwellers, who need less protection from the sun, have lighter skins. And the fairest skins of all may be found in cool and cloudy climates like those of Northern Europe.

The varieties of adaptation

While genetic adaptation requires many generations to become apparent, physiological adaptation develops quite soon after the individual is exposed to a new environment. This adaptation occurs on at least two levels: there is the short-term acclimatization, exemplified by the uneasy adjustment that visitors make to La Paz after a few weeks; and the total adaptation that natives of any area exhibit to the part of the world in which they live. In addition to these physiological forms of adaptation, there is a psychological one, habituation, which develops from the individual's willingness to accept the difficulties of an environment—such as extremes of heat or cold—without paying much attention to them or letting them interfere with normal function.

But man's capacity to adapt physiologically to an alien environment is limited. The expeditions that have climbed Mt. Everest have demonstrated that people can tolerate heights as great as 21,000 feet for several weeks, yet no one who has climbed the mountain ever claimed that he could live at this height indefinitely. At such an extreme altitude, a process of physical deterioration sets in which eventually forces the climber down. Apparently men from sea level cannot become fully adapted to any height above 15,000 to 17,000 feet.

The oxygen masks that brought success to Sir Edmund Hillary and Tenzing Norkey when they scaled Mt. Everest in 1953 symbolize the technological and social adaptation which, over the years, have increasingly come to supplement man's biological means of coping with his environment. The trend toward this kind of adaptation started long ago. If man had been compelled to depend on physiological or genetic adaptation alone, he would probably never have left the semitropical regions in which he first evolved. Man has neither fur nor feathers, and does not carry the fat that could give him the kind of whole-body protection blubber affords the seal. Without some such equipment, he could not have ventured from the warmest parts of the earth until he learned to use fire. And even then, his range remained limited; fire is not enough to protect the naked body against cold winter nights. It was only when he developed ways of turning animal skins into warm clothing that man could move to the cooler climates.

The hands of the fishermen

Even without protective clothing, man can achieve partial physiological adaptation to cold, but the evidence about whole-body adaptation is meager and inconclusive. Fishermen whose hands are frequently exposed to cold water develop better circulation in their hands, and thus a greater local resistance to low temperatures. In the same way, if one were to dunk one finger into an ice-water bath for 20 minutes four times a day, he would find that after a month this finger would become exceptionally resistant, remaining quite warm even during the dunking.

In the autumn of 1957, eight Norwegian students volunteered to camp out for six weeks high on a mountain range, clad only in light summer clothing, in order to permit scientists to study the process of physiological adaptation. At night, when the temperatures ranged from 41° F. to freezing, the boys lay naked in sleeping bags consisting of one blanket and a thin outer covering. The first few nights were unpleasant; the boys shivered so much they could not sleep. But they gradually became acclimatized, and soon were able to sleep soundly through the night. After their six weeks of hardening, the students returned to a base laboratory, where their reactions to sleeping out of doors were compared with those of a control group. Measurements of skin temperature showed that as the temperature of the air fell throughout the night the experimental group stayed warm from head to toe, while the controls' skin temperature dropped steadily, especially of the feet. Measurements of oxygen consumption showed that both groups of boys burned up more

SPHERE AND CYLINDER represent the body shapes best adapted respectively to cold and hot extremes of weather. Though the figures above are equal in volume, the cylinder has one third more surface area. In the Arctic, a short, plump person loses body heat through a minimum of skin surface. In tropical climates height is an advantage, providing a larger surface through which the body loses heat by perspiration and radiation.

oxygen than they would have normally, in order to produce more heat. But only in the experimental group did this expedient effectively maintain body warmth.

The Norwegian experiment was conducted at temperatures which require an increase in metabolism of about 50 per cent to maintain normal body heat. At such temperatures, the homeostatic mechanisms of adaptation to cold can still be expected to work efficiently. That they do is evident not merely from this study, but from an experience common to everyone who lives outside of tropical climates; in midwinter a temperature of 50° F., which would seem exceedingly cold in summer, feels quite warm if it has been immediately preceded by freezing days.

Staying warm at the poles

In areas of extreme cold like the polar regions, however, physiological adaptation no longer suffices. Without clothing, no man can burn up enough fuel in his own body to make up for such cold as this. Yet the Eskimos have functioned successfully in such climates for centuries. Remarkably well adapted socially and technologically, they live in warm houses and wear warm clothing, exposing only their faces and hands to the outside air. "The clothes the Eskimos wear in the Arctic during the coldest months of the year, January or February, weigh under ten pounds, which is a good deal less than the winter equipment of the average New York businessman," reported explorer Vilhjalmur Stefansson. "At −40° F., a Mackenzie Eskimo . . . sits outdoors and chats almost as comfortably as one does in a thermostat-regulated room. . . . While indoors [among the Eskimos] we were living in a humid, tropical environment; when outdoors we carried the tropics around with us inside our clothes. Neither indoors nor out were we using any considerable part of the caloric value of our food in a biological struggle against chill."

The Eskimos' traditional diet of blubber and meat also served to help them adapt to their surroundings; fat and protein are more effective in producing body heat than carbohydrates. But when the white men came to the North, they disrupted the old social structure, and the Eskimos' health began to collapse. Western clothes began to replace fur garments; carbohydrates, in the form of bread, pancakes and syrup, became a major part of the diet. Before the white man came, the Eskimos were free of dental caries. Today virtually every Westernized Eskimo child has cavities in his teeth. Tuberculosis has taken a terrible toll among both children and adults. Altogether the Eskimos provide a dismal example of the way in which "civilization" can ruin the lives of primitive peoples—a process that is occurring more and more frequently as the people of Stone Age cultures take on the white man's ways.

Just as the ancient Eskimos learned to adapt to their cold world, so

A HIGH-ALTITUDE RESEARCH CENTER, this hut 19,000 feet above sea level near Mt. Everest served as laboratory and living quarters for Sir Edmund Hillary and a group of scientists and mountaineers in the winter of 1960-1961. They stayed five and a half months, but never adapted completely to the height. Men lost from one to three pounds a week, and grew progressively less fit.

other primitive peoples have adapted to conditions so rough as to seem to a Westerner incompatible with life. The nomadic bands of naked aborigines who wander the deserts of South Africa and Australia build no shelters, find their drinking water in mudholes, and subsist on a diet of wild plants and insects.

Occasionally the environment defeats all but the hardiest members of a group, who alone manage to adapt. In Pueblo Indian villages in the U.S., youngsters swim happily in streams that also serve as sewers, laundries and sources of drinking water. These particular children, perhaps because of their genetic endowment or because they have developed immunities, have adapted to a myriad of microbes. But these are the lucky ones. Among the Pueblo Indians the death rate for infants under a year old is four times as high as it is among other Americans. This brutal form of adaptation by survival still prevails throughout the world's underdeveloped areas, where a staggering infant mortality has for centuries been considered inevitable. It is, however, on the wane as people are coming to realize that many of these deaths can be prevented.

Western society, which has succeeded in forestalling most such deaths, has in the very process raised a host of other health problems. Western youngsters are carefully sheltered. They have properly balanced diets, made up of bacteriologically clean foods. To a large extent, they are spared the stress of infection. The rewards are obvious; less obvious is the price that some of these children may have to pay for their relatively effortless existence.

The problems of the germ-free

Some clues as to what this price may be are offered by a recent study of germ-free animals. Domestic mammals, delivered by Cesarean section under aseptic conditions, were raised in environments that protected them from contact with any detectable microorganisms. Although they grew to a normal size and were capable of reproducing, the animals exhibited many physiological abnormalities. For one thing, their intestines did not develop properly, with the result that when they were first exposed to a normal environment, they suffered severely from infectious illnesses that have no effect on animals raised in ordinary circumstances. Life without germs left them, initially at least, at a disadvantage when they entered the germ-filled world.

Comparative studies of domesticated and wild rats also suggest that an easy life has certain drawbacks. It has been found that rats raised in the laboratory for generations are less able than wild rats to provide for themselves, to fight, and to resist fatigue, toxic substances or disease. The adrenal glands, which play a role in the body's defenses against stress, are smaller and less effective in the laboratory rat than in his wild cousin. The thyroid gland, which helps regulate metabolism, is less active. On the other hand, the gonads, which are responsible for sex activity and fertility, develop earlier in the laboratory animal, which is therefore much more fertile. Tame rats are also better adapted to the laboratory. In this environment, wild rats often die. Tame laboratory rats live peacefully in groups—while caged wild rats fight among themselves—and can resist such stresses as handling and stroking. Thus, it is impossible to make a flat statement about the susceptibility or resistance of either group to disease; each adapts to its environment.

The careful sheltering of children is only one aspect of a growing tendency in Western countries to avoid physical challenges, escape discomfort and change the external environment to suit man's desires. With the flick of a switch, modern man can turn on air conditioning or central heating; he can thus keep the temperatures of his office or home the same all year round, and he can even bring this comfort to the North Pole and the tropics. Seasonal shortages of food never need affect him: he may have the diet of his choice virtually anywhere in the world and at any time of year. He can seal out noise in a cork-lined room, while soothing background music helps him relax. New drugs can help him control his biological and emotional responses. He has become so expert in altering his physical environment that he is beginning to believe he no longer needs the biological mechanisms of adaptation which have enabled him to survive until now.

The challenge of the future

Yet the speed with which man is altering his environment makes it inevitable that future generations will have to cope with situations almost unimaginable today. And if man cannot adapt to them, his future is bleak. Physicians, like generals, are always prepared to fight the last war. They can easily handle the health problems that were produced by the first Industrial Revolution, but they have not yet evaluated the effects on man of the revolutions of automation and transportation that are now taking place. These changes tend to make life more and more effortless. But the human body, like the human mind, is geared to respond to challenges. Studies of prehistoric animals have shown that any creature that cannot adjust to changing conditions faces extinction. For man, an environment in which life is too undemanding physically may be a death warrant.

Nobody knows, for example, how man's health may be affected by the ways in which he has upset his built-in biological rhythms. Practically every aspect of human physiology has a daily as well as a seasonal rhythm, both of which coincide with the rhythms of the natural environment. Until the last century, man lived in the dark for long hours during the winter months, as many primitive people do today. But modern man is exposed to bright light for 16 hours a day throughout the year. The effect of this unnatural environment on him is not yet clear. It is known, however, that light increases gonadal activity in many animals. Indeed, most chicken farmers maintain a high level of egg production throughout the year by keeping the hen house illuminated much of the time. Yet when an experimental flock of chickens was exposed to unremitting light, the birds became so susceptible to disease that the entire flock was wiped out within three years.

Tampering with man's biology

The ease with which men jet from one time zone to another may also have undesirable effects on health. An airline pilot who flies from New York to Tokyo is still on New York time, biologically speaking, when he arrives at his destination. It is several days before his pulse rate, body temperature, digestive processes and secretion of adrenal hormones adjust to Tokyo time—and by then he may be on his way back to New York. After several such trips he may develop various unpleasant symptoms: he may lose or gain weight, and suffer from insomnia and a general sense of tension and irritability.

The increasing tendency of humans to jam themselves into smaller and smaller areas may pose a new sort of hazard. Crowding has always been considered a danger to health because of the threat of microbial disease and contagion it carries, and because it has been generally associated with poor sanitation and poor housing conditions. Today science is learning that crowding has many other undesirable effects. Experiments have demonstrated that it produces dramatic changes in hormonal activity among laboratory rats, and these hormonal changes may be responsible for the lowered fertility and higher death rate that developed when the animals were forced to live crowded together. Hormonal changes may also explain such extreme disturbances of behavior as those seen in the lemmings' so-called "march to the sea," during which thousands and thousands of the animals destroy themselves. It remains to be seen whether crowding also produces changes in man's hormonal secretions and behavior.

TWO WAYS OF ADAPTING to the equatorial climate of hot days and cool nights result in radically different dwellings. The West African, who wears few clothes, needs a thick-walled, small-windowed mud hut *(above)* for comfort by night. The hut is hot by day, but stays warm through most of the cool hours. Better-clad Malaysians, who worry less about the night chill, build well-ventilated houses *(below)* that stay comfortable all day.

So little is yet known about the conditions to which man will have to adapt in the future that the best safeguard is to preserve and further develop his general adaptability. In wartime, all kinds of people from all kinds of environments manage to survive and to function under appallingly difficult circumstances: in the field under various conditions of weather and terrain, in concentration camps, in prisoner of war camps, on life rafts without food or drinking water.

Because man may again be compelled to endure these nightmares, the

U.S. armed forces have sought methods of cultivating man's adaptive potential. No systematic body of knowledge has yet been accumulated. But it does appear that suitable techniques of experimentation can be worked out. They need not be as drastic or time-consuming as the six-weeks' exposure to cold the Norwegian students endured. British Royal Navy scientists conducted experiments on artificial acclimatization to humid heat; they found that when Londoners were exposed to such heat only two hours a day for a few days or weeks, they became just as well adapted to the climate as were the members of a matched group who lived in Singapore for 18 months. As long as they were re-exposed to humid heat every few days, the Londoners could maintain their adaptation indefinitely. And as new knowledge is accumulated, other procedures of adaptation will undoubtedly be developed to build up resistance to other stresses and strains, somewhat as vaccines now build up immunity to a variety of microbial infections.

Hopefully, science will one day discover methods of training both body and mind so that they can achieve maximum adaptability to all sorts of unpredictable situations. For health is not a passive condition. It is a changing, dynamic state, which gives each man the ability to take advantage of his entire mental and physical potential, and to make his life creative, rich and full.

On the Frontiers of Health

Of all the world's health problems, the most pressing and difficult are those of the underdeveloped countries. In these lands medical facilities are inadequate, and diseases flourish which have been wiped out in almost every other part of the world. In Nigeria each doctor serves 38,000 people; in the United States the ratio is 1 to 670. In 1961, when not one U.S. case of smallpox was reported, records showed 45,204 cases in India. The list of grim statistics could be extended almost indefinitely. For years, the medical missionary (opposite) provided primitive peoples with their only enlightened help in the fight against disease. The missionary's efforts continue, but he is no longer alone. More than 100 nations—from the U.S. to the U.S.S.R. and from Gabon to El Salvador—are now joined in the World Health Organization. In 1950, when WHO was still in its infancy, 130,000 people died of cholera. In 1960, the figure was 13,000—a 90 per cent drop.

A MISSIONARY'S HEALING TOUCH
An American missionary-nurse, Mrs. Lee Kindberg, changes the dressing on the burned foot of an Indian boy in Peru. Mrs. Kindberg and her husband, Will, spend seven months a year among the Campa Indians, combining religious instruction with the work of healing, and providing the only modern medical aid available to a people who live 250 miles away from the nearest hospital.

WEAVING A NEW LIFE

A blind boy in India learns to make mats from coconut palm fronds at the Tata Agricultural Center, an international school for the blind which also trains teachers of the handicapped.

The Theory of Education

In the underdeveloped countries, superstition, ignorance and fear are as much a threat to health as are the microbes of disease. In Nigeria, the centuries-old custom of rubbing the navels of the newborn with vegetable oil often resulted in death from tetanus, introduced by the salve. Yaws, a highly contagious and disfiguring disease endemic in many parts of Africa and the Philippines, could be eradicated if the people in these regions were not ignorant of even the simplest rules of hygiene. Vaccination could render smallpox and diphtheria ineffectual—were it not that many primitive peoples are more afraid of the hypodermic needle than they are of disease.

In the 1950s, education programs were launched in Africa, Asia and Latin America, to teach some of the basic rules of public health and disease prevention. Rehabilitation programs were also set up. In the underdeveloped lands, disabilities like lameness and blindness, often the consequence of disease, have traditionally doomed their victims to live as beggars and outcasts. Vocational training (left) now redeems many of the handicapped to lead useful lives.

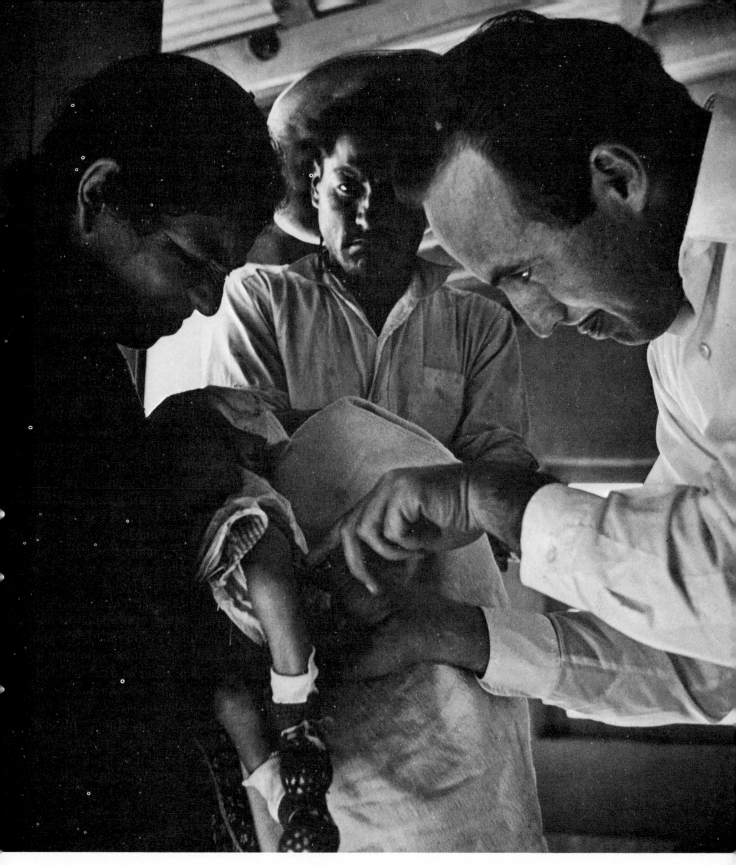

STUDYING THE SYMPTOMS

A Liberian mother peers at photographs of people with yaws so that she can recognize its symptoms. Along with a public education program, Liberia is waging a medical campaign against yaws: health workers travel the country, treating victims and teaching prevention.

PAIN FOR PREVENTION

Held by a wincing mother while a grim father looks on, a child is inoculated against diphtheria in the Mexican village of El Refugio. To raise standards of health and eliminate some of the most common communicable diseases, Mexico requires its newly graduated physicians to work for six months in substandard areas, giving free treatment to those who cannot afford to pay.

Careers in Health for Women

When the Sudan's Khartoum Nursing College opened in 1956, only six young women could persuade their parents to let them enroll: nursing was not considered respectable for well-bred girls. Yet by 1963 the freshman class had 20 students—capacity enrollment. The quiet revolution these figures suggest is going on in many underdeveloped countries as prejudice and custom give way to the recognition that women, as well as men, must participate in fighting disease. In these lands, where medical personnel are in desperately short supply, major emphasis is on educating auxiliary workers to aid physicians: women are being trained as nurses, midwives and technicians. In 1961, the proudest graduates of Syria's midwifery course were 18 grandmothers—average age 55—who had returned to school to learn modern ways of practicing their ancient skill.

A LOOK INSIDE THE BODY

American nurse Barbara Knapp *(second from left)* uses a model of the body to instruct Indian and African student nurses at the multiracial Aga Khan Hospital in Nairobi, Kenya. The hospital, founded in 1958 by Kenya's Mohammedan colony, is a training and treatment center.

A MODERN MIDWIFE FOR THE BUSH

Joyce Binney of Ghana, a British-trained midwife, starts into the bush to make a house visit. In addition to being trained in modern obstetrical methods, midwives in the underdeveloped countries learn to advise mothers on nutrition and other aspects of postnatal infant care.

CARRIER OF A NEW DISEASE

A researcher extricates a migrating bird from a net in the grasslands of southern India, where research is being carried out on Kyasanur Forest disease, a virus-caused fever discovered in 1957. Infected ticks carried by certain birds transmit the virus. To discover how the disease is spread geographically, the bird is banded, then released, and its migrations are followed.

On the Trail of Infectious Diseases

In the underdeveloped countries, infectious illnesses are a major threat. Their cost is high, not only in suffering, but in the permanent damage they can do. In some rural sections of India, trachoma *(right)* has weakened the vision of 80 to 90 per cent of the population; in some African villages, blindness is so common that ropes are strung to guide women on their way to the village well and bamboo poles laid to guide men planting in the fields. The first step in the control of many diseases is to find their carriers and then trace the paths by which they travel. These two activities are a major concern of medical research in the new nations.

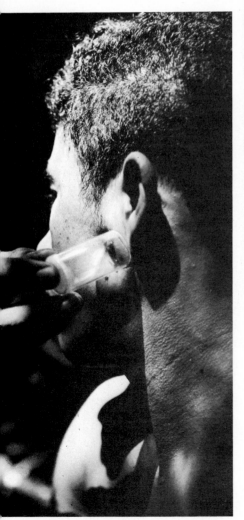

CARRIER OF A DREAD DISEASE
A research worker investigating the role of flies in the spread of trachoma nets one on the face of a young Indian boy. Although flies are known to be one major carrier of this disease, their precise role in transmitting it is unclear. A World Health Organization trachoma team is working with researchers at Gandhi Eye Hospital in Aligarh in hopes of finding the answer.

CARRIERS OF VIRUS DISEASES
A volunteer provides a meal for a Tabanid fly, one of hundreds of bloodsucking insects under study at the Belém Virus Laboratory in Brazil, to learn the role of biting insects in transmitting the infectious diseases called "arboviruses," which are prevalent in the Amazon River Valley.

A Massive Assault on Malaria

In 1955 the World Health Organization began to mobilize the largest medical army in history—190,000 strong—for an all-out war on the illness that the ancient Indians called the "King of Diseases": malaria. When the battle began, more than one and a half billion people lived in the shadow of malaria; only two years before, it had struck half the population of Taiwan and killed so many Bolivian children that in some sections of the country all youngsters were known as *chuccho puchus*—malaria leftovers. But by 1963, under the massive assault mounted by WHO, malaria had been effectively brought under control in 25 per cent of areas where it once ravaged the population. In time the illness may be curbed to such an extent that the onetime "King of Diseases" will have lost its standing as a major menace to the health of the world.

FINDING THE VICTIMS
A health worker takes a blood sample from the hand of a villager in Puerto San José, Guatemala. The woman shows no malaria symptoms, but analysis may disclose she is harboring its parasite. Periodic checks to find such hidden carriers are important in the antimalaria campaign.

CURBING THE PARASITES
A member of a field unit distributes chloroquine pills to youngsters in Puerto San José. A suppressant rather than a cure, chloroquine reduces fever within 24 hours and destroys the parasites in the blood within 48, but must be taken periodically for continuing protection.

EXTERMINATING THE CARRIERS
A malaria control team *(opposite)*, carrying pumps and buckets of insecticide, travels on elephant-back to a remote village in India to spray its houses against the *Anopheles* mosquito. The team will make periodic return visits for four years, in hopes of eradicating the insect.

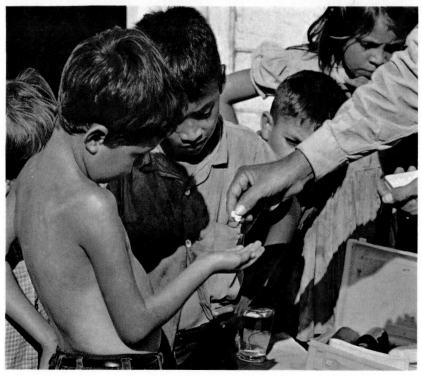

Pure Water:
A Basic Necessity

When health workers in Africa asked village women to name their single greatest need, they answered, "Water." That response would have been echoed throughout the underdeveloped world, where water supplies are not only insufficient but also impure, and often carry the microbes of such diseases as cholera, typhoid and amoebic dysentery. In rural areas, one well or water hole may serve an entire community. Of the quarter billion people living in the cities of Africa and Asia, only one in five has piped water in his home and fewer than half have water within half a mile. In the new nations, the development of a network of sanitary pipelines is high on the priority list. Where water lines have been laid, the effects on health have been immediate and dramatic: in one rural section of India, the death rate from cholera fell 74 per cent in five years.

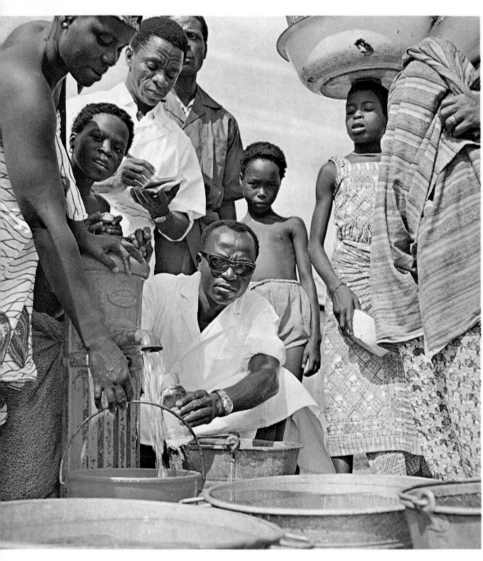

IN QUEST OF PURITY
A sanitation team collects a sample of water from a public fountain in Lomé, capital of Togo, Africa. Such samples are then tested to discover if pathogenic bacteria are present. Often water supplies like this are an open invitation to infection since water is the breeding ground for many communicable-disease organisms, like those that cause trachoma and gastroenteritis.

IN SEARCH OF WATER
Trying to reach water in a drought-dried well, villagers in the Madura district of India carry buckets of silt up to the surface by hand. Such laborious methods must still be used during the dry season in many parts of the underdeveloped world, where piped water is not available.

A WONDER OF MODERNIZATION
A farmer in Hyderabad, India, compares his old bullock-driven pump with a new engine-driven model he purchased with the help of a state loan. The water brought up by the power pump flows into stone-lined irrigation canals, to supply moisture for the farmer's growing crops.

A Square Meal in the Offing

In one Oriental language, *beriberi* means "I can't"—because the illness, caused by lack of vitamin B1, produces paralysis in its victims. Beriberi is but one of the many diseases common in countries where people subsist on diets short on most nutritional essentials. Poor diet also contributes to poor health indirectly by weakening the body, and thus making it vulnerable to infection. But as increasing attention has been paid to nutrition, much of the undernourished world has had its diet supplemented by both artificial additives *(left)* and by natural food sources that were not made use of previously.

A DIETARY SUPPLEMENT

A Guatemalan woman pours a protein supplement, Incaparina, onto a *tortilla* before baking it. Incaparina is one of several newly developed protein powders, derived primarily from pea- nuts, cereals and fish, now added to the usual protein-poor diets of some underdeveloped countries. Where these supplements are in use, the incidence of disease has dropped sharply.

A NECESSARY FOOD

Preschool children in Moundou, southern Chad, drink milk sent them by UNICEF—the United Nations International Children's Emergency Fund. Milk, the single best food for growing bodies, is in short supply in many of the new nations, and must be imported in powder form.

A NEW SOURCE OF FOOD

Villagers net a catch at a fish farm in Orissa, India, which was established by the Indian Government and UNICEF in a program to improve nutrition. Because fish is an excellent source of protein, some of each catch is reserved to be given to young mothers and children.

Planting Seeds— and Ideas

"If you are planning for a year," an old Chinese proverb says, "grow rice. ... If you are planning for one hundred years, educate the people." In the modern world, the proverb has been revised: "Whether you are planning for one year or one hundred, grow rice *and* educate the people." Rice is the basic food of more than half the world's population: in many Asian languages, the words for "rice" and "food" are the same. Yet in the Far East, which produces 90 per cent of the world's supply, farming methods are still primitive and scientific breeding to improve quality is unknown. Ways must be found to grow more rice by old-fashioned methods and also to grow better rice, capable of supplying the nutriments necessary for health. At the International Rice Research Institute in the Philippines, all these problems are under study. A joint project of the Rockefeller and Ford Foundations, this eight-million-dollar venture, staffed by scientists from all over the world, illustrates both the need the underdeveloped countries have for assistance in achieving health and the response that this need is now finding.

SEARCHING FOR A SUPERIOR STRAIN
Cheng-seng Huang, of Taiwan, examines stalks of rice grown in a plant-pathology greenhouse at the International Rice Research Institute. The rice is one of 8,000 varieties being tested to find those best suited to meet the nutritional needs of an expanding world population.

190

The Advance of Life Expectancy

Today the average American can confidently expect to live to be 70 but, as the graph below indicates, it has taken centuries for life expectancy to reach that point. At any given time during most of human history, relatively few men could count on living to be 60. Scientists believe that man's potential life-span has always been the same—about 100 years—but until fairly recent times, disease cut most men down long before nature aged them.

The graph is based on figures derived from examinations of skeletons, tombstones and legal documents, and from modern census counts. It shows the estimated life expectancy of the average male at age 15—that is, at an age safely past the diseases of childhood—in various populations from Neanderthal man (250,000 to 40,000 B.C.) to the present. Note that a Bronze Age youth could expect to reach 40, but life expectancy dropped into the thirties again in the cities of Greece and Rome, where epidemics were common. The estimate for 18th Century Philadelphia, lower than that for 17th Century Breslau, probably reflects the squalid conditions of a young city in the New World; Philadelphia too suffered from epidemics at the time.

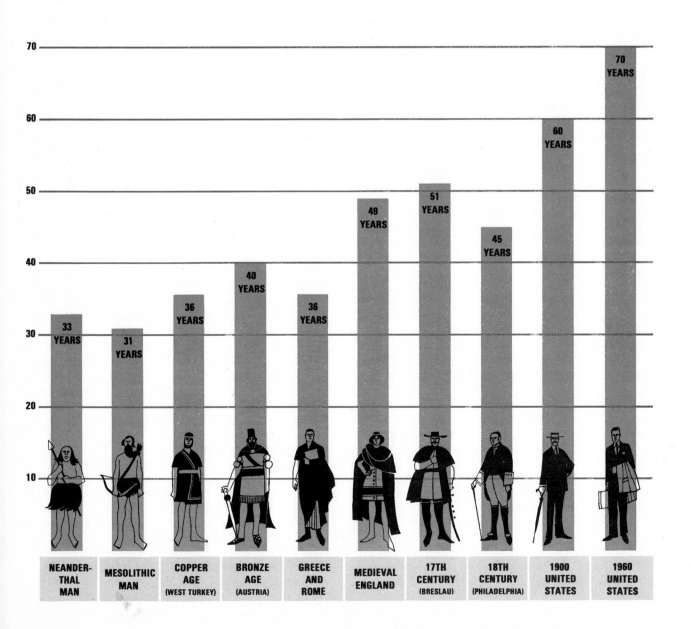

NEANDER-THAL MAN	MESOLITHIC MAN	COPPER AGE (WEST TURKEY)	BRONZE AGE (AUSTRIA)	GREECE AND ROME	MEDIEVAL ENGLAND	17TH CENTURY (BRESLAU)	18TH CENTURY (PHILADELPHIA)	1900 UNITED STATES	1960 UNITED STATES
33 YEARS	31 YEARS	36 YEARS	40 YEARS	36 YEARS	49 YEARS	51 YEARS	45 YEARS	60 YEARS	70 YEARS

FURTHER READING

History

†Atkinson, D. T., *Magic, Myth and Medicine.* Premier, 1958.

Bettmann, Otto L., *A Pictorial History of Medicine.* C. C. Thomas, 1956.

Dubos, René, *The Unseen World.* The Rockefeller Institute Press, 1962.

Garrison, Fielding H., *An Introduction to the History of Medicine.* W. B. Saunders, 1929.

Biography

Dubos, René, *Louis Pasteur: Free Lance of Science.* Little, Brown, 1950.

Lambert, Royston, *Sir John Simon.* MacGibbon & Kee, 1963.

†Olmsted, J.M.D., and E. Harris, *Claude Bernard.* Colliers Press, 1961.

Williams, Greer, *Virus Hunters.* Alfred A. Knopf, 1959.

Man and Health

Cannon, Walter B., *The Wisdom of the Body.* Norton, 1963.

Clark, Randolph Lee, and Russell W. Cumley, eds., *The Book of Health.* Van Nostrand, 1962.

Coon, Carleton S., *The Story of Man.* Alfred A. Knopf, 1962.

Dubos, René, †*Mirage of Health.* Doubleday, 1961. *Man Adapting.* Yale University Press, 1965.

Fiennes, Richard, *Man, Nature and Disease.* Weidenfeld & Nicolson, 1964.

Man and Disease

Burnet, Sir MacFarlane, *Natural History of Infectious Disease.* Cambridge, 1962.

Davidson, Sir Stanley, A. P. Meiklejohn and R. Passmore, *Human Nutrition and Dietetics.* William R. Wilkins, 1964.

Dubos, René, and James G. Hirsch, eds., *Bacterial and Mycotic Infections of Man* (4th edition). J. B. Lippincott, 1965.

Dubos, René, and Jean, *The White Plague.* Little, Brown, 1952.

Horsfall, Frank L., and Igor Tamm, eds., *Viral and Rickettsial Infections of Man.* J. B. Lippincott, 1965.

Ingle, Dwight, *Life and Disease.* Basic Books, 1963.

McCollum, Elmer V., *A History of Nutrition.* Houghton Mifflin, 1957.

*McKusick, Victor A., *Human Genetics.* Prentice-Hall, 1964.

White, Paul D., *Heart Disease* (4th edition). Macmillan, 1951.

Man and His Environment

*Carson, Rachel, *Silent Spring.* Houghton Mifflin, 1952.

Herber, Lewis, *Our Synthetic Environment.* Alfred A. Knopf, 1962.

*Selye, Hans, *The Stress of Life.* McGraw-Hill, 1956.

*Available in paperback edition.
†Available only in paperback edition.

ACKNOWLEDGMENTS

The editors of this book are indebted to Dr. Lawrence E. Hinkle Jr., Associate Professor of Medicine and Clinical Associate Professor of Medicine in Psychiatry, New York Hospital-Cornell Medical Center; and to the following persons and institutions: John H. Adler, International Monetary Fund, Washington, D.C.; American Diabetes Association, Inc.; Dr. J. Lawrence Angel, Curator, Physical Anthropology, Smithsonian Institution; Dr. Alexander Bearn, Professor, The Rockefeller University; Honorable Arthur J. Benline, New York City Department of Air Pollution Control; Dr. Eric J. Cassell, Clinical Instructor of Public Health, Dr. Benjamin H. Kean, Clinical Associate Professor of Medicine (Tropical Medicine), and Dr. James R. McCarroll, Associate Professor of Public Health, Cornell University Medical College; Dr. Robert H. Daines, Professor and Research Specialist, Plant Pathology Department, and Dr. John B. Schmitt, Professor of Entomology, Rutgers University; Dr. Carolyn Denning, The Babies Hospital, Columbia Presbyterian Medical Center, New York City; the Departments of Public Health, Berkeley and Los Angeles, Calif.; Dr. Ivan F. Dunaief, Bronx Eye and Ear Hospital, Bronx, N.Y.; Dr. William K. Emerson, Chairman and Associate Curator, Department of Living Invertebrates, American Museum of Natural History; Dr. Angela Folsom, Veterans Administration Hospital, Danville, Ill.; Jerry Hagan, Public Relations, General Motors AC Spark Plug Division, Flint, Mich.; Dr. David Hammerman, Associate Professor of Medicine, Albert Einstein College of Medicine, Bronx, N.Y.; Joseph T. Hogan, Principal Chemist, Rice and Sweet Potato Investigations, Food Crops Laboratory, U.S. Department of Agriculture, New Orleans, La.; Dr. Pascal J. Imperato, Fellow, Division of Hygiene and Tropical Medicine, Tulane University School of Medicine; Professor William T. Ingram, School of Engineering, New York University; Dr. Leo Kartman, Scientist Director, Plague Suppressive Laboratory, U.S. Public Health Hospital, San Francisco; Dr. J. Austin Kerr, Research Officer, Malaria Eradication Branch, Pan American Health Organization; Frederick G. Kilgour, Librarian of the Yale Medical Library, Yale University; Dr. Marvin Kuschner, Professor of Pathology, New York University School of Medicine and Director of Laboratories, Bellevue Hospital Center; Dr. Olivier Leroux, Medical Liaison Officer, World Health Organization, United Nations; Dr. John Marchand, Associate Member, and Dr. Ade T. Milhorat, Director, Institute for Muscle Disease, New York City; E. W. Martin, Advertising Manager, Fine Chemicals Division, Hoffmann-La Roche, Inc., Nutley, N.J.; Dr. Mervyn Meggitt, Department of Anthropology, University of Sydney, Australia; William J. Mellor, Division of Public Information and Education, Los Angeles County Air Pollution Control District, Los Angeles, Calif.; Muscular Dystrophy Association of America; National Cystic Fibrosis Research Foundation; National Hemophilia Foundation; A. J. Parenti, Chief, Operational Services Unit, UNICEF, United Nations; Dr. Anthony Payne, Chairman, Department of Epidemiology and Public Health, Yale University; Dr. Cornelius B. Philip, Principal Medical Entomologist, Rocky Mountain Laboratory, U.S. Public Health Service, Hamilton, Mont.; Public Information Office, World Health Organization, United Nations; Harold Romer, Director, Bureau of Sanitary Engineering, New York City Department of Health; Dr. Harold Schwartz, University of California School of Medicine, Los Angeles, Calif.; Dr. Carl E. Taylor, Director, Division of International Health, School of Hygiene and Public Health, The Johns Hopkins University; Dr. Lester J. Tepley, Senior Nutritionist, Food Conservation Division, UNICEF, United Nations; Donald A. Trauger, National Tuberculosis Association, New York City; the United Epilepsy Association; Alice D. Weaver, and Nancy Willey, Rare Book Division, The New York Academy of Medicine; Kay Wise, The Rockefeller University; World Health Organization Photo Service, Geneva, Switzerland; Dr. Pedro W. Wygodzinsky, Associate Curator, Department of Entomology, American Museum of Natural History; Dr. Meir Yoeli, Associate Professor, Department of Preventive Medicine, New York University Medical Center; and the staff of the Raritan Bay Project, Division of Water Supply and Pollution Control, Public Health Service, Metuchen, N.J.

INDEX

Numerals in italics indicate a photograph or painting of the subject mentioned.

PICTURE CREDITS

The sources for the illustrations which appear in this book are shown below. Credits for the pictures from left to right are separated by commas, from top to bottom by dashes.

Cover—Arnold Newman.

CHAPTER 1: 8—Larry Burrows. 10—Ann Parker and Avon Neal courtesy Art in Amer-
ica Co., Inc. 11—Culver Pictures. 13—Eric Schaal courtesy Yale University Medical
Library. 15—The Bettmann Archive. 17—Drawings by left Martin and Alice Pro-
vensen; center Allan Mardon—Leo and Dianne Dillon; right Bernard Perlin—
David Klein. 18, 19—Drawings by Martin and Alice Provensen. 20, 21—Drawing by
Allan Mardon. 22, 23—Drawings by Leo and Dianne Dillon. 24, 25—Drawings by
Bernard Perlin. 26, 27—Drawings by David Klein. 28, 29—Drawings by Otto van
Eersel.

CHAPTER 2: 30—Fabrizio Parisio courtesy Capodimonte Gallery, Naples. 32—The
New York Public Library. 33, 34—The Bettmann Archive. 35—Drawing by Patricia
Byrne courtesy Dr. Edward C. Wendt. 36—The New York Public Library. 37—
Culver Pictures. 39—David Lees. 40—Left Dr. Harry Most, New York University
College of Medicine; right Keturah Blakely. 41—Top Clay Adams Inc., New York
City, and Dr. Harry Most, New York University College of Medicine. 42—Keturah
Blakely. 43—Left Clay Adams Inc., New York City, and Dr. Harry Most, New York
University College of Medicine; top Ylla from Rapho-Guillumette—Dr. Bruce Mc-
Millan, School of Public Health and Tropical Medicine, University of Sydney, Aus-
tralia. 44—John Moss from Photo Researchers, Inc.—Roger Tory Peterson from
Photo Researchers, Inc. 45—Dr. Harry Most, New York University College of Med-
icine—Keturah Blakely. 46—Keturah Blakely. 47—James Simon from Photo Re-
searchers, Inc.—Dr. Harry Most, New York University College of Medicine, Aldo
Margiocco. 48—Keturah Blakely—N. J. Kramis, Rocky Mountain Laboratory, U.S.
Public Health Service. 49—N. J. Kramis, Rocky Mountain Laboratory, U.S. Public
Health Service. 50—Keturah Blakely—Leo Kartman, CDCA San Francisco Field
Station, U.S. Public Health Service. 51—Howard Sochurek.

CHAPTER 3: 52—Heath courtesy Philadelphia Museum of Art. 55—The New York
Public Library. 56—Bottom Phil Brodatz courtesy The New York Academy of
Medicine. 58, 59—Drawings by Nicholas Fasciano courtesy Charles Pfizer & Co.
60, 61—The New York Public Library. 63—Ullstein Bilder Dienst, Berlin. 64—The
Bettmann Archive, Interfoto M.T.I. 65—Eric Schaal—courtesy Harvard Medical
School. 66—Eric Schaal courtesy Yale University Medical Library—Radio Times
Hulton Picture Library. 67—Eric Schaal courtesy Yale University Medical Library.
68, 69—Wellcome Historical Medical Museum—courtesy the Royal College of Sur-
geons; right Dr. Heinz Zinram courtesy the Royal College of Surgeons. 70, 71—Center H. Roger Viollet. 72—Bundesgesundheitsamt, Robert Koch Institut, Berlin—
The Bettmann Archive. 73—Brown Brothers.

CHAPTER 4: 74—Douglas Faulkner. 77—Bottom drawing by Patricia Byrne. 79—
Drawing by Nicholas Fasciano, prepared by permission from an illustration copy-
right © 1954 by *Scientific American* Inc. All rights reserved. 80, 81—Drawings by
Nicholas Fasciano. 82—Phil Brodatz courtesy New York Academy of Medicine.

83—Drawings by Nicholas Fasciano. 85, 86, 87—Drawings by Joseph Lombardero.
88, 89—Drawings by Otto van Eersel. 90, 91—Drawings by Joseph Lombardero.
92, 93—Drawings by Otto van Eersel. 94, 95—Drawings by Joseph Lombardero,
Otto Van Eersel. 96, 97—Drawings by Joseph Lombardero.

CHAPTER 5: 98—Ted Russell. 100—Drawing by Otto van Eersel. 102—Drawing by
Anthony Saris. 105—Drawing by Anthony Saris. 107, 108, 109—Zvonko Glyck.
110—Ted Russell. 111—Drawing by Matt Greene. 112, 113—Zvonko Glyck. 114—
Courtesy Department of Plant Biology, College of Agriculture, Rutgers University. 115—Left drawings by Patricia Byrne; right drawings by Adolph E. Brotman.
116, 117—William Vandivert, Department of Public Works.

CHAPTER 6: 118—The National Foundation-March of Dimes. 120—Drawing by Otto
van Eersel. 122—Drawing by Patricia Byrne. 124—Drawing by Nicholas Fasciano
—drawing by Otto van Eersel courtesy Dr. Harold Schwartz. 125—Drawing by
Otto van Eersel. 126—Drawing by Nicholas Fasciano. 129—Drawings by Otto van
Eersel. 131—Fritz Goro. 132—Don Uhrbrock, Institute for Muscle Disease—Fritz
Goro. 133—Fritz Goro. 134, 135—Gordon Tenney except bottom left Don Uhr-
brock. 136, 137—Fritz Goro. 138, 139—Horst Ehricht—Joe Clark, Art Shay (2). 140
—Courtesy Veterans Administration Hospital. 141—Left and top right Gordon
Tenney. 142—Zvonko Glyck except bottom right Henry Groskinsky. 143—Henry
Groskinsky.

CHAPTER 7: 144—Drawing by Robert Osborne. 147—Drawing by Boris Artzybasheff.
149—Drawings by Fred Hausman. 152—Drawings by George V. Kelvin. 155—
Drawing by George V. Kelvin courtesy Lawrence E. Hinkle and Harold G. Wolff,
Annals of Internal Medicine. Vol. 49, December 1958. 157—Arthur Leipzig. 158—
The American Museum of Natural History. 159—The American Museum of Natural
History—Manchete. 160, 161—Arthur Leipzig. 162, 163—Wilfred Thesiger. 164—
Carl Mydans. 165—Carl Mydans—Wide World. 166, 167—Carl Mydans.

CHAPTER 8: 168—Ted Polumbaum courtesy Roche Medical Image. 171—Drawings
by Charles Mikolaycak. 172—Drawing by Nicholas Fasciano. 175—Drawings by
Nicholas Fasciano. 177—Cornell Capa from Magnum. 178—P. Shinde from United
Nations World Health Organization—Paul Almasy from United Nations World
Health Organization. 179—Arthur Leipzig. 180, 181—Marc and Evelyne Bernheim
from Rapho-Guillumette. 182, 183—Paul Almasy from United Nations World
Health Organization, Paulo Muniz, Homer Page from United Nations World
Health Organization. 184—P. N. Sharma from United Nations World Health Or-
ganization. 185—Douglas Faulkner. 186, 187—Howard Sochurek except left Marc
and Evelyne Bernheim from Rapho-Guillumette. 138, 189—Douglas Faulkner,
Marc and Evelyne Bernheim from Rapho-Guillumette—UNICEF. 190, 191—Art
Rickerby. 193—Drawings by Allan Mardon. Back Cover—Charles Mikolaycak.